Contents

Foreword

It is an alarming paradox that while people with a learning disability have poorer health than other members of the community, they make less use of health services.

In 1995, the Department of Health proposed a three-part strategy, *The Health of the Nation: A Strategy for People with Learning Disabilities*, to address this obvious anomaly. First, people with a learning disability need help to make healthy choices about their lifestyle – this is referred to as health promotion. Second, we know that illness among people with learning disability is often not detected in the early stages when it can be treated quickly and effectively. We need to become better at helping people with a learning disability to find out about illness as soon as possible – this is referred to as health surveillance. Finally, when people with a learning disability seek medical advice, it is important that they are provided with the same standards of care as everyone else – this is about removing inequalities in health care.

The resources contained in this new edition of *Health-Related Resources for People with Learning Disabilities* will help families and informal carers, staff working in services, and people with learning disabilities themselves to become more aware of health issues and the things that they can do to promote good health and ensure that poor health is treated quickly and effectively.

It describes over 100 resources that have been published since the first edition in 1995 and it is good to know that, in addition to being summarised in this reference book, they can also be scanned on the HEA's database HealthProm*is* via the internet. This publication will play a key role in the provision of improved health care for everyone with a learning disability.

John Harris

John Harris
Chief Executive, The British Institute of Learning Disabilities

Introduction

Health-related resources for people with learning disabilities was originally produced by the Health Education Authority (HEA) in 1995 to provide a comprehensive source of information about resources that could be used to promote health and access to health services for people with learning disabilities. The information was also made available on the national database for health promotion in the Health Promotion Information Centre (HPiC) at the HEA. Since 1995 the database has been updated regularly. This book is the revised edition and includes those resources added to the database since 1995, plus those resources produced from 1993 onwards that were in the original publication.

This is one of several health-related resources databases commissioned by the Department of Health and developed by the HPiC. As the national centre for health promotion information and advice in England, the HPiC supports and develops the capacity for effective health promotion at local, national, and international level. These databases are one of the services provided by the HPiC to support local health promotion.

The databases are targeted at population groups that are traditionally hard to reach, have particular health needs, or for whom it is difficult to find appropriate resources. To date, the database series includes health-related resources for:

- Black and minority ethnic groups.
- People with learning disabilities.
- Older people.
- Young people (11 to 19 years old).
- Men.

Background

In England and Wales around 20 people in every thousand have a learning disability that necessitates support of some kind. About three or four per thousand of the population have severe learning disabilities and need frequent support with some aspect of daily living.[1]

During the past 20–30 years, the circumstances in which many people with learning disabilities live have changed fundamentally, in terms of both where they live and the services they use. The implementation of community care, the re-organisation of local authorities that purchase and/or provide services at local level, and changes in the National Health Service (NHS) have transformed many of the institutions and services that people with learning disabilities regularly use. In addition to this, the growth of the self-advocacy movement has had an impact on both service provision and people's expectations.

There have also been changes within the education system, with the introduction of the National Curriculum and the drive to improve excellence in schools for all children. It is estimated that up to 20 per cent of school children may need special educational help at some stage in their school careers.[2]

These social and institutional changes have shifted the context in which health education and promotion take place. The number of people with learning disabilities who live in institutions dropped by well over half between the late 1970s and early 1990s, while the number of residential places increased dramatically during the same period. This growth continues, and in the four years to 1996–97 the number of places in staffed residential homes for people with learning disabilities increased by about 6000.[3] The rise in life expectancy of people with learning disabilities also means that more parents continue to be carers into their old age and many people with learning disabilities now outlive their parents. As increasing numbers of people live independently with varying degrees of support, and are encouraged to make everyday decisions about their lives, learning about health and how to stay healthy becomes essential. This has implications for the education and health needs of those with learning disabilities.

In 1995 the Department of Health's *Health of the Nation* strategy for people with learning disabilities[1] highlighted the fact that this group experiences the same health problems as the rest of the population but is more likely to experience certain conditions and to be ill. For example, general health problems, sensory impairments, mental health problems, epilepsy, and other physical disabilities are more common in people with learning disabilities. This group, however, is less likely to use the health services than the general population, and when they do the experience can be negative. The Department of Health strategy emphasised the need for accessible health education that involves health professionals, teachers, social service workers, parents, and carers, as well as people with learning disabilities. It encouraged services to promote healthy lifestyles and independent functioning, and to develop special programmes of health promotion. The emphasis was on programmes with an individual focus, reflecting the main thrust of the *Health of the Nation* strategy on lifestyle issues such as diet, exercise, and sexual health.

In 1998, following a change of government, the consultation paper *Our Healthier Nation*[4] put forward proposals for a contract for health. This places greater emphasis on tackling the causes of ill-health, including social and economic factors as well as lifestyle issues, and on improving access to quality services. The health needs of the worst off in society are given prominence and the government is committed to reducing health inequalities. Social exclusion can have damaging health consequences and the government has firmly identified the need to address the causes of this – poverty, unemployment, poor physical and social environments, illness, and disability – in partnership with the public, private, and voluntary sectors.

As with the previous health strategy, *Our Healthier Nation* proposes priority areas for action. The four priorities are:

- Heart disease and stroke.
- Accidents.
- Cancer.
- Mental health.

It also highlights three key settings:

- Healthy schools – focusing on children.
- Healthy workplaces – focusing on adults.
- Healthy neighbourhoods – focusing on older people.

Local and health authorities are expected to work together to improve health and to identify local health needs with a particular emphasis on the socially excluded and those who need support. The main vehicles for translating the national contract into local action are Health Improvement Programmes and Primary Care Groups, and Mencap is calling for the specific needs of people with learning disabilities to be addressed. A series of national initiatives underpins the new approach to public health – for example, Health Action Zones, Healthy Living Centres, the Healthy Schools Initiative and Wired for Health, Welfare to Work, and the New Deal for young people.

In 1997 the Secretary of State for Health highlighted the fact that people with learning disabilities are disadvantaged in terms of access to general health services and that services can be insensitive to the needs of this group. He emphasised the rights of people with learning disabilities to access health promotion and health services, and encouraged collaborative working between departments to ensure that this group is included.[5] Recent research by Mencap[6] confirms that the NHS is failing to provide an equal service to people with learning disabilities – for example, women are left out of health screening, and the uptake of dental, vision, and hearing tests is lower among people with learning disabilities. The study also highlights a lack of awareness and negative attitudes on the part of healthcare staff.

A guide for NHS managers and professionals, *Signposts for Success*,[7] was issued by the Department of Health in 1998. This aims to improve services and access to them for people with learning disabilities. It sets out good practice and covers the quality and range of services that people with learning disabilities can expect, including routine health checks and specialist help and support.

Health-related resources

The provision of health information has a part to play in the strategy to improve the population's health. Health-related resources are important tools for health promotion, particularly for people who have special needs or who may have difficulty accessing general health information. For people with learning disabilities, the information and the way it is presented can be a barrier, and there is clearly a need for accurate and understandable information produced in appropriate formats.

In the mid-1990s, when the database was originally developed, it was apparent that professionals who worked with people with learning disabilities wanted more information about health-related resources. The database filled this gap, providing details of 164 titles. Over the years this database project has highlighted various trends. Resources have become more carefully targeted and the range of topics has increased. The growth of the self-advocacy movement in particular has had a significant impact on the production of resources, with far more being developed both in consultation with and by people with learning disabilities.

The guidance on using resources to work with people with learning disabilities that was included in the original publication is reproduced again in this publication as the advice remains current (pages 15–21).

Terminology

Throughout this document, the term 'people with learning disabilities' is used. Since 1991 the Department of Health has used this term to replace the term 'mental handicap' and to highlight 'a change of emphasis in the philosophy of care and in the values which inform our thinking'. The term emphasises learning potential, equality of citizenship, and 'a commitment to thinking of people with learning disabilities as individuals in their own right'.[8]

In the Department of Health's strategy for people with learning disabilities,[1] the term learning disability is described as meaning:

- the reduced ability to understand new or complex information, to learn new skills (impaired intelligence);
- the reduced ability to cope independently (impaired social functioning);
- which started before adulthood, with a lasting effect on development.

Where specified by the producer of the resource, terms like 'mild', 'moderate', 'severe', or 'profound' learning disabilities are used to describe the intended audience. These definitions of levels of impairment are based on intelligence testing and performance measures.[8] They do not have precise boundaries and are not completely reliable as accurate indicators of abilities or needs, but they do point to a broad level of ability at which a resource may be targeted.

Blind and partially sighted is the term used to indicate a range of sight difficulties.

The term 'facilitator' is used throughout to refer to anyone who supports someone with a learning disability in making use of a health education resource. This may include health professionals, social services workers, other people with learning disabilities, teachers, tutors in further education, advocates, parents or carers, and support workers. Where a resource is intended to be used in a specific setting, more precise terms are used – for example, in reviews of resources intended for schools the reference is to 'teachers'.

There are many types of resource that can be used or adapted for use to promote health-related work with people with learning disabilities. The term 'resources' is used to describe a variety of formats – videos, audio cassettes, manuals and guides, booklets, games, training packs, and models. The term multi-media refers to a resource that includes a variety of formats, as well as to disks and CD-Roms. Posters were included in the original publication but are excluded in this revision. Although leaflets, postcards, and posters can be invaluable in health-related work, they are often locally produced and have a shorter 'shelf-life', making them unsuitable for inclusion in this publication.

The project

The aims of the health-related resources database are to:

- Provide up-to-date information about current resources that promote health and healthy lifestyles and access to services.
- Highlight gaps in provision.

Original development

The database was developed initially in 1995 following a national search to identify currently available health-related resources for people with learning disabilities. Over 5000 statutory, voluntary, and commercial organisations were contacted for details of resources they produced, distributed, used, or knew about. These organisations included health and education, social services, voluntary, community and self-advocacy groups, professional organisations concerned with health, and producers and distributors of resources. Information was also requested via relevant journals and newsletters.

A number of criteria were laid down for inclusion in the database. Resources were included if they:

- could be used in education about health and healthy lifestyles, health services and how to use them, or particular conditions and diseases;
- were nationally available, either for sale or hire;
- were produced from 1987 onwards (although some earlier resources were included if nothing similar was available);
- (or the activities they described) were primarily for people with learning disabilities.

The focus of the database is on resources that can be used directly with people with learning disabilities, often with the help of a facilitator. Resources aimed at professionals were included if they contained direct suggestions for work with people with learning disabilities. Resources primarily for professional development purposes were excluded, although these can be used to supplement understanding and skills for working with people with learning disabilities. In some instances, for example where the audience is people with complex and profound disabilities, resources are more likely to address professional skills with suggestions for practice. Resources from other countries were included if they were easily obtainable, and there was no similar resource produced in the UK.

The database was first made available via the HPiC's electronic database and in a published format. Information was also available by contacting the HPiC National Enquiry Service and requesting a database search, the results of which were posted out to enquirers.

Continued development

Since the original search and publication of the database, the HPiC has continued to identify resources by scanning relevant journals, catalogues, and publicity material. The material is regularly reviewed and added to the national database for health promotion, HealthProm*is*. This can be accessed directly on the website http://healthpromis.hea.org.uk or at http://www.hea.org.uk/hpic where the HPiC pages of the HEA's website are located.

Although this is the second edition of the published database, the criteria for inclusion remain the same except that the cut-off date is now 1993 to ensure that the information is as current as possible. Many of the resources produced prior to 1993 are no longer available. Those that are still available are retained on the HealthProm*is* database but are not included in this publication. Of the resources produced between 1993 and 1995 that were in the original publication, 43 are still available and are retained in this updated edition.

Since 1998, the reviews also include some guidance on the appropriateness of the resource for use with blind and partially sighted people. As more than one in three children with sight difficulties also has additional disabilities, including physical, learning, sensory, and communication disabilities, this advice may help users select the most appropriate material.

Findings from the original search and subsequent updates

The original search identified 164 resources that met the criteria for inclusion. A further 28 resources were found subsequently and included in an Appendix of 'Late and forthcoming resources', making a total of 192 health-related resources for people with learning disabilities. Of these, 103 resources pre-dated 1993 and were excluded from this edition. Since 1995 nearly 100 resources have been added.

Comparing the number identified between 1995 and 1998 with the 164 identified over an eight-year period, it is clear that the production of health promotion resources for this audience is increasing.

The *Review of the NHS role in learning disability services* (1996)[9] identified a need for written materials with few words, in large print for people with sight difficulties, in different languages, and with symbols and clear life-like pictures. This suggests that posters can be as effective as leaflets. Models were also considered particularly useful, as were videos, audio cassettes, and games.

The review also identified a number of areas where resources were lacking. These included: mental health; physical activity; cervical screening; stress; epilepsy; alcohol; exposure to the sun; smoking; using health services; weight loss; and recognising illness and pain. The review highlighted the potential conflict between promoting individual choice and risk taking; for example, eating certain foods and smoking may be recognised as health risks but may also be seen as positive, independent choices.

The original search in 1995 revealed a lack of available or up-to-date resources on certain issues for people with learning disabilities. Two of the most notable gaps were resources concerned with cancers and mental health, despite these topics being key *Health of the nation* (1992)[10] target areas. Also lacking were resources concerned with smoking, alcohol, and drug misuse.

Since then, few resources have been produced that deal with cancers and mental health, despite these remaining key government priorities.[4] However, the number of substance misuse resources has increased four-fold, with the main emphasis being on illegal drugs and smoking. No resources specifically about alcohol were found, although alcohol is often addressed within the broader context of substance misuse.

The largest number of resources identified in the original search and in subsequent updating, concern sexual health and personal relationships. This reflects the broad scope of this category but also a greater acknowledgement on the part of professionals and service providers that people with learning disabilities have sexual health education needs. The number of parenting resources has more than doubled since 1995.

Three other areas – advocacy, communication, and resources to support independent living in the community – account for a large proportion of the available resources. The growth of the self-advocacy movement has influenced the increase in resources that promote self-help and personal responsibility for everyday living. Although they are not directly health related, this revised edition also includes a few resources that address issues relating to the criminal justice system. These resources explore the rights of people with learning disabilities, explain the legal process, and relate their experience of crime and the judicial system.

During the update period, 1995–1998, there has been a substantial increase in the number of resources focusing on consultation and service provision, within both the health service and community care services. This increase reflects changes in service delivery and the overall rise in people's expectations and rights. Some of the resources explain basic medical procedures such as visits to the doctor or the dentist, others focus on improving communication between professionals and people with learning disabilities, and a few explore how people with learning disabilities can complain when they are not satisfied.

One 'workplace' resource with a focus on safety was identified. With the emphasis on supporting disabled people to find and take up employment, this is an area with potential for growth. There is an opportunity to explore the production of resources to support the New Deal for Disabled People and the National Disability Development Initiative (NDDI).

Since the original publication, there has been a decrease in the number of resources produced on arts and leisure, play, physical activity, food and nutrition, and growth and development.

A positive development throughout the 1990s is the visual representation of people with learning and physical disabilities in resources. Almost all the videos produced since 1994 use actors with learning disabilities or show people with learning disabilities talking about their lives. For example, resources about abuse include the survivors talking about their experiences, in their own voice, rather than being described by someone else.

It is also clear that people with learning disabilities are beginning to be more involved in the production of resources and that piloting and evaluation of resources is more common. Although most resources do not include a description of the development process, it is clear that several are produced by experienced workers and carers. Consequently, resources produced for children are less likely to be promoted as suitable for use with adults with learning disabilities.

Resources for people with learning disabilities remain almost exclusively in the English language, although the images used increasingly include people from black and minority ethnic groups. More resources are accompanied by support materials for carers and families.

Formats

A wide range of formats is included in this publication – videos, training packs, books, manuals and guides, games, audio cassettes, and models.

Over the years there have been several changes in the type of resource produced. The 1995 search found that 'newer' resources tended to be more visual – for example, videos, card sets, and photographs. They were also more interactive and creative – for example, games, workbooks, and drama resources. These resources tended to be more flexible than those produced in the late 1980s. Since 1995 there has been a decrease in the number of games and cards produced, although these are sometimes included as one element of a pack or multimedia resource. Slides as a medium have all but disappeared, largely replaced by the potential of video. Video is the largest single format group produced since 1995. Books and packs continue to use plenty of illustrations, and a few audio cassettes have been produced.

In 1995, computer software and CD-Roms were not included in the database because of the speed with which technology was changing. However, it was acknowledged at the time that this medium could be especially accessible to some people with learning disabilities as programs and keyboards can be adapted to meet individual needs. Interactive multimedia resources have enormous potential for providing learning experiences that were previously unavailable. They offer the opportunity to create virtual experiences that people themselves can control, and to engage several senses at once. However, few resources have appeared in this format.

Reviews and critical reading

Once a resource is identified, it is reviewed by professionals who work with people with learning disabilities. The reviews aim to provide a snap-shot of the resource to help others decide whether or not to purchase or use the resource. They are not a substitute for facilitators thoroughly previewing the resource themselves before using it.

Each review covers:

- The target audience.
- The aim of the resource.
- A brief description of the contents.
- Whether any supplementary or support material is needed.
- Any notable omissions or errors.
- Equal opportunities, in particular whether or not the resource reflects differences in ethnicity and culture, gender, sexuality, disability, and age. More recently, the review includes guidance on whether the resource also can be used with blind and partially sighted people.
- How the resource can be used and how it was developed, if this is known – for example, whether people with learning disabilities were involved in the development of the resource and if it was evaluated.

Some of the original reviews were read and commented upon by other experts to ensure that they were fair, well written, and informative. Minor changes were then incorporated into the reviews. The HEA thanks the reviewers and critical readers who are listed in Appendix 1.

Frances Bird
Victoria Fitch

References

1 Department of Health (1995). *The Health of the Nation. A Strategy for People with Learning Disabilities.* London: HMSO.

2 Department for Education and Employment (1997). *Excellence for all children. Meeting special educational needs.* London: The Stationery Office.

3 Department of Health (1997). *Health and personal social services statistics for England.* London: The Stationery Office.

4 Department of Health (1998). *Our Healthier Nation.* London: The Stationery Office.

5 *New health for people with learning difficulties.* Department of Health Press Release (September, 1997).

6 Mencap (1998). *The NHS – health for all?* London: Mencap National Centre.

7 Department of Health (1998). *Signposts for success in commissioning and providing health services for people with learning disabilities.* London: The Stationery Office.

8 Thompson D. (1993). *Learning disabilities: the fundamental facts.* London: Mental Health Foundation.

9 *Review of NHS role in learning disability services.* Health Education and Promotion Focus Group (1996). (Unpublished.)

10 Department of Health (1992). *The health of the nation: a strategy for health in England.* London: HMSO.

How to use this book

Entries

The resources are listed alphabetically by title, ignoring definite and indefinite articles (such as 'The' or 'A'). All the resources are available in English only, unless otherwise stated.

Entries for each resource include information about its format, the cost, the producer or publisher, the date of publication, and the distributor. Contact details for the distributors are given in Appendix 2. The information contained in this publication was correct at the time of going to press. However, details such as price may change over time and items may be withdrawn or become out of print. It is advisable to check these with the distributor.

Where producers specify a target audience this information is included in the review. However, some producers are not specific about the audience and the reviews try to give a sense of who the resource might be used with, how, and in what settings.

Indexes

The resources are indexed by topic, some under more than one topic. These topics represent broad categories. The topics index has been amended since the original publication in 1995. The aim is to standardise the topic headings across the various health-related resources databases and to bring the index in line with the HPiC's Health Promotion Thesaurus now in use. The Thesaurus is used to assign key words to resources entered on the database.

For the purposes of the learning disabilities database, the main changes to the original Topics Index include:

- Access to health services and Access to community care services replace Consultation and service provision.
- Alcohol is now a separate topic.
- Bereavement is now indexed as Death and dying.
- The body replaces Growth and development.

- Communication includes language development, translation, English for speakers of other languages (ESOL) materials, and specific communication disorders. It no longer includes communication skills, which are now under Inter-personal and social skills.
- Drugs and solvents are now a separate topic.
- Health conditions and illnesses includes specific conditions rather than each being listed separately.
- Leisure now includes arts, crafts, drama, and play.
- Living in the community includes practical life skills only.
- Mental health includes well-being, emotional resilience, and specific mental illness.
- Nutrition replaces Food and nutrition, with food safety indexed as Food hygiene.
- Personal hygiene replaces Everyday care and personal hygiene.
- Physical, emotional, and sexual abuse replaces Abuse.
- Smoking is now a separate topic.

There is also an index listing resources by format.

Choosing and using resources

The reviews contained in this publication are intended as a guide to help you select the appropriate resource for the health issues or topics you wish to address and the audience with whom you are working. Always preview a resource yourself before using it, to make sure you are familiar with the issues it raises, and that you have any additional information required. If you are working with support workers and interpreters, it is helpful also to familiarise them with the resource.

The following section, *Using resources to support health education for people with learning disabilities*, provides some useful guidance on the process of learning and how to maximise the effectiveness of health-related resources when working with this audience.

Sources of further information

Health Promotion Information Centre (HPiC)

The HPiC at the HEA is the national centre for health promotion information and advice. It offers a range of services to professionals with an interest in health promotion, including access to HealthProm*is*, the national database for health promotion. This is regularly updated and includes documents such as research reports, key papers, journal articles, specialist books, multimedia resources, and a series of resource databases, with links to various websites and other databases. The reviews included in this book, and those relating to the other health-related resources databases, can also be accessed on the web directly at http://healthpromis.hea.org.uk or via the HPiC pages of the HEA's website at http://www.hea.org.uk/hpic. You can conduct your own search and check the latest additions

to the database, following the guidance provided on the website. A search of the database can also be requested by contacting the HPiC via:
Tel: 0171 413 1995; Fax: 0171 413 2605; e-mail: hpic.enquiry@hea.org.uk

If you or your organisation have developed a health-related resource for people with learning disabilities that you would like to have considered for inclusion in the database, please send it to:

Health-Related Resources Database Manager
HPiC
Health Education Authority
Trevelyan House
30 Great Peter Street
London SW1P 2HW

Local health promotion agencies

Local health promotion units and agencies are a valuable source of information and support. Many have resources available for loan and reference libraries, and may supply leaflets and posters. Specialist health promotion staff may be available to advise on health promotion strategies, issues, and topics, and to provide training. They will also have details about local initiatives. The address and phone number of your local unit or agency can be found in the telephone directory under the name of your local health authority.

British Institute of Learning Disabilities (BILD)

This is a national organisation supporting people with learning disabilities, their families, and those who work with them. Its principal activities are education and training. It produces two quarterly publications about information and resources – *Current Awareness Service*, a monthly listing of new materials, resources, and events, and *Bulletin*, a quarterly collection of recently published papers on topical themes. BILD also publishes a range of books, manuals, and periodicals for professionals including: the *British Journal of Learning Disabilities*, a quarterly journal containing articles on service innovations and therapeutic approaches; *Mental Handicap Research*, which reports on research on service provision in the UK and overseas; and *The SLD Experience*, a termly newsletter for those involved in the education of children with severe learning disabilities.

BILD can also help with more specific requests for information about contacts and resources, and has a library that is open to anyone who wishes to use it for reference purposes. For further information, contact:

British Institute of Learning Disabilities
Wolverhampton Road
Kidderminster
Worcestershire DY10 3PP
Tel: 01562 850251; Fax: 01562 851970

Makaton Vocabulary Development Project (MVDP)

MVDP is a charity that promotes the use of the Makaton Language and Communication Programme. It is used extensively in the UK as well as internationally. The MVDP co-ordinates a national network of Makaton tutors who provide a variety of training courses and workshops appropriate for carers, families, teachers, therapists, administrators, and all support staff. A wide variety of resource materials and support services is available – videos of signs; guidelines to teach and use the signs and symbols; books of Makaton symbols and pictures; a parent/carer distance training pack; a membership scheme for all Makaton users; and a research information service. For further information contact:

MVDP
31 Firwood Drive
Camberley
Surrey GU15 3QD
Tel/Fax: 01276 61390; e-mail: mvdp@makaton.org; Website: http://www.makaton.org

National Development Team (NDT)

The NDT is an independent agency based in Manchester that works to improve opportunities for people with learning disabilities. It aims to encourage the development of good quality services, better legislation and policy in health, social care, education, employment, housing, and transport. The agency supports and advises about good practice through research projects, conferences, workshops, and publications.

The NDT has recently completed a major programme of work on health gain and people with learning disabilities, and is involved in the development of good practice in primary healthcare services. For more information, contact:

National Development Team
St Peter's Court
8 Trumpet Street
Manchester M1 5LW
Tel: 0161 228 7055; Fax: 0161 228 7059; e-mail: office@ndt.org.uk;
Website: http://www.ndt.org.uk

Using resources to support health education for people with learning disabilities

The late Ann Craft, Senior Lecturer, Department of Learning Disabilities, University of Nottingham.

Caroline Downs, Research Officer, Teacher at Oak Lodge School and former Further Education Lecturer, University of Nottingham.

The most effective learning for people with learning disabilities, particularly those with severe disabilities, is through either experiential learning or concrete – or virtual – representations of real life. When it comes to health and sex education this, clearly, presents problems and resources become a vital means of imparting information and skills. The challenge in teaching sex education to people with learning disabilities is to simulate situations/experiences in as concrete a way as possible while retaining the dignity and privacy that using abstract materials or talking hypothetically would afford. Resources make this possible.

The wide range of materials now available and reviewed in this book can undoubtedly greatly enhance our teaching and learning on the subject of health and sex education. They can transform what might otherwise be an incomprehensible explanation into an easily understood, memorable lesson. Resources can make learning more interesting and more fun, and make it easier for the student to generalise new skills and knowledge from the learning situation into real life. They can make teaching so much easier: bright visual materials, for example, will capture the imagination of the otherwise uninterested student; models or line drawings permit us to explore with dignity aspects about ourselves or our bodies that we could not otherwise explore.

Furthermore, packaged resources save us, as educators, from time-consuming quests after 'the right picture' or from desperate attempts to draw or model clearly to illustrate our points. Indeed, it is very difficult to imagine describing and explaining to students certain bodily functions or aspects of relationships without resources, and they comprise a support for our teaching from which both we and our students benefit enormously.

It is important, however, to remember that this is precisely what a resource is: a *support* for our teaching. Inevitably any resource will only be as effective as the understanding and creativity of the teacher; the glossiest, most state-of-the-art resource will be of limited use if presented in an unimaginative or inappropriate manner.

Once you have identified and obtained a resource, before using it, it is important to go through certain processes:

- Be aware of the policies and guidelines that exist in your place of work. Also think carefully about people you may need to consult or are required to consult – for example, your manager, other professionals, parents.
- Be clear about what you are trying to teach and why you are trying to teach this – for example, as a stage in an overall health education programme, in response to a student (apparently) requiring this information or this particular skill, etc.
- Be sure that you feel comfortable with what you are trying to teach.
- Consider your own and/or your colleagues' need to undertake some training and development work in this area.
- Try to put yourself in your students' shoes – how do you think the individual or group of students perceives this aspect of themselves in relation to the world?
- Be aware of the learning styles of individual students.
- Be familiar with the resource and evaluate it critically, asking yourself if it is appropriate for this particular student/group.

Be aware of policies and guidelines

Most establishments will have policy documents setting out the philosophy and rationale to the health and sex education undertaken there. Probably there will also be guidelines that can protect you (as well as your students and clients) in any work you undertake – providing you abide by them!

Parents will need to be consulted if your student is under 18; it may also seem appropriate, on occasions, for parents to be informed for clients above this age. Parents can be an invaluable source of support, reinforcing learning at home. They may be reticent about some aspects of health and sex education and need to be reassured that such education will be appropriate and responsible.

Health and sex education does not take place in a vacuum and some consultation with your manager should take place. Colleagues who also teach your students may need to be involved, or at least informed.

Be clear about what you are trying to teach and why

Policies and guidelines will help guide your thinking in terms of what is deemed appropriate for your students about certain topics. If you decide that you are going to teach an individual about masturbation, for example, you will need to be clear about what it is you think she or he needs to learn – for example, privacy, hygiene implications, different people's attitudes towards it, and the practicalities – and relate these to your establishment's guidelines.

You need to be clear about how you will know if the student has grasped/understood what you want to teach; that is, how will she or he behave differently/how might she or he respond to a question posed or to a situation presented? If this is not clear in your mind at the outset it will be difficult to know whether your teaching and your use of the resource have been successful.

Be comfortable with what you are about to teach

If you do not feel comfortable enough to be open and honest about topics that you may not be accustomed to discussing freely, you are likely to make oblique statements or use euphemisms. 'Going to bed with someone' or 'sleeping with them' may have certain connotations for most of us; but for many people with learning disabilities, this will be taken literally and therefore be misunderstood. If you feel embarrassed or uncomfortable you will be conveying all sorts of messages at odds with what you know to be important to your student(s) and that, in theory anyway, you are endeavouring to put across. The so-called hidden curriculum is a powerful phenomenon – any feelings and attitudes that the teacher may have will be evident to her or his students and will be assimilated by them, probably to a greater degree than the content she or he was trying to put across!

If you feel uncomfortable, it is likely that you will be unable to articulate clearly what you mean. For example, 'do you want to go to the toilet?' should mean that and that alone. It should not also be used to mean: 'it looks like you are masturbating; I don't want you to do that in here and the only private place around here is the toilet, so please go there.'

A teacher needs, firstly, to be sure that she or he is the right person to be teaching the student(s) and, secondly, to work out ways in which to set up the situation so that she or he feels all right and the student(s) feel comfortable.

Consider staff training needs

People with learning disabilities have the right not to be the recipients of the personal attitudes towards sexuality of their carers. Craft[1] points to the following as being one of six sexual rights and values:

> 'The right not to be at the mercy of the individual sexual attitudes of different care-givers'.

Our own individual attitudes towards sexuality are in fact often 'untutored' in other words; perhaps because we seldom discuss our views concerning sexuality with others in the course of our daily lives, they tend to remain unaired, unchallenged, and unmodified by the views of others, in contrast to our attitudes towards more openly discussed issues. Similarly, we all hold cultural and religious values which are important to us and so do our students and clients, their parents and carers. Left unchallenged, each of us is likely, understandably, to assume that 'my' views are the only views, the right views, with the result that clients may be on the receiving end of differing – and conflicting – opinions.

We need, therefore, to create the opportunity to discuss our beliefs via staff training, for example, or in discussion with other parents/carers, in order that we can make decisions with awareness.

It is also important that we have anticipated and thought through these issues and our emotional responses to them – and have these written in the form of policies – in order that we do not react in a knee-jerk fashion to events or questions that may occur. It is important also to predict events that might occur and how we will respond to them – for example, if a student disrupts a session, or a new student joins the group.[2]

Reflect on how student(s) perceive the world

We can all probably relate many stories that demonstrate a student's perception of a situation being completely different from that which we, as educators, had assumed. Often this may not be discovered until afterwards, although sensitive questioning of students who are able to communicate their views may pick this up at the time.

Assumptions that we as educators generally make in response to a situation or a picture can involve quite subtle or sophisticated interpretations, which are often inaccessible to the people with whom we work, either because the image is outside of their experience and not one they would easily imagine, or because an intuitive leap is required to make (our) sense of the image. For example, a picture of a perpetrator of abuse, who to us may quite clearly be about to harm a person, may be interpreted by a client as the person being rude to the perpetrator because the former (i.e. the person) is pulling a nasty face.

Thus we may not be justified in assuming that practising putting a condom on to a toothpaste dispenser – or even on to a penis model – is a useful activity if the student has not fully grasped that the model 'stands in place of' a penis, and indeed stands in place of his own penis or the penis of a partner prior to penetration.

We need, therefore, to become quite skilled in our questioning and sensitive in our observations to be sure that our teaching has been successful. Checking out an individual's comprehension is very important; frequently our concern, as educators, to ensure that the concept is grasped, means we may fail to recognise a gap in a student's understanding. Complacency in our own teaching may lead us to assume comprehension when a student says to us 'wear a condom, don't get AIDS', and thus not to check out his or her full understanding. False assumptions of this nature may only later become apparent as a result of real-life evidence.

Resources may help us to explain and illustrate situations; they are, however, only as powerful as our skills as educators.

Be aware of the learning styles of individual students

The use of commercially produced resources in teaching depends on a student's being able to grasp the concept of one thing representing something else; this was referred to in the discussion of the use of a penis model (section above), as was the possible danger of making assumptions and using a resource in an inappropriate situation.

At the beginning of this chapter we looked at the role of the resource in terms of its simulating real-life experiences and making as concrete as possible situations/actions where experiential learning is impossible because of the subject matter.

Different resources will vary, of course, in their level of 'concrete-ness' and this, in conjunction with the preferred learning styles of individual students, needs to be taken into account when deciding on the appropriateness or otherwise of a particular resource.

For most students with learning disabilities (those with moderate to severe learning disabilities, whose receptive language may be quite good and who, often, are well able to grasp the concept of one thing representing something else) most resources are potentially accessible and their success is reliant on the creativity of the teacher/educator.

Most resources are primarily visual – videos, pictures, line drawings and photographs, posters, illustrated books and slides, account for the majority. For many students these will, of course, be quite appropriate; videos have enormous appeal and are highly motivating – particularly those with soap-opera-type formats – and books and pictures are well-established media in most students' learning experiences. It is important to remember, though, that resources have been produced with general relevance as well as specific target audiences in mind, and it is therefore up to individual teachers/educators who know their own students' needs to review the appropriateness of the materials and adapt them to meet those needs.

Of the five senses, we tend to make most use of vision followed by, perhaps at some distance behind, hearing. For all students, the more senses that can be engaged during presentation of material and learning, the better, and for some students this will be vital. Providing appropriate experiences using smell, taste, and touch often taxes us, as teachers, to the utmost, and combined use of different resources may help us to do this. For people with sight difficulties, the use of tactile information is clearly necessary. Pictures may be made more concrete, and therefore more memorable, for all students by making them kinaesthetic. This can be done by raising the outline with string, plasticine or sandpaper, and encouraging finger tracing.

For students with very severe or profound learning disabilities and with additional sensory impairments, abstract information is often not sufficient on its own. Where people are not able to use photographs or line drawings or pictograms/symbols in everyday life, most of the more commonly used resources for health and sex education will be inaccessible.

Many such students will be using 'Objects of Reference' or 'Tangible Symbols' as a method of communication precisely because they have not yet learned to associate an abstract concept – that is, a picture – with the object it actually represents in real life. Creating Objects of Reference for some issues in health and sex education has become quite commonplace, although this is not as yet well documented. Thus, a woman student may come to associate a particular bag with sanitary towels, and can therefore communicate about these both receptively and expressively. Other areas and activities are more difficult to ascribe Objects of Reference – 'private' body parts and/or experiences for instance – and, the building up of the association between actual object and the Object of Reference symbolising it involves frequent everyday use, which is unlikely in the case of highly personal issues.

It is not possible here to explore learning styles and the devising of appropriate strategies and 'resources' for health and sex education for the relatively small percentage of students whose current level of development and understanding precludes symbolic use of materials for teaching. This was an area of research undertaken in the Department of Learning Disabilities at the University of Nottingham.[3]

For most students with learning disabilities, imaginative use of the range of resources reviewed here will be appropriate and successful.

Be familiar with the resources you are planning to use

It is of paramount importance to remember that the resource is a *support* for our teaching – it is not the teaching itself. Having selected a resource that appears to have promise, we need to get to know it well, think about the needs of the student(s) who is/are going to be using it and then be prepared to adapt it to meet their needs.

When using a video with a group, for example, it may be appropriate to play a particular excerpt, show stills, use picture only – or indeed sound only – to highlight particular aspects. Some students find it difficult to concentrate on more than one mode at once. Some videos can be productively role-played as well as discussed. Pictures may be too big, too small, have too much detail which results in confusion and so on, even if the content is right for a particular individual or need. Teachers may want to reduce them in size, blow them up, cut parts out, add colour or whatever seems right, to meet their particular need. In some instances, it may be useful to chop up pictures and use the people from one picture superimposed on the background of another, with the part under focus coloured in or emphasised in some other way. Photographs of individuals in the group can be used alongside commercially produced materials to emphasise the point. Soundtracks can be made to accompany certain pictorial resources.

For some students, it may be unacceptable to show images of naked people. Responses to this situation will depend on existing policies and guidelines and perhaps the possibility of negotiating with parents or advocate where this would seem to be appropriate.

Teachers will be aware of favourite games; many pictorial resources are amenable to being chopped up and made into a board game, with a dice for throwing to which students respond, perhaps in role; and card games – matching pairs, memory games, happy families and so on. The limits are bounded only by the flexibility and creativity of the teacher.

Be constructively critical of a resource so that you can balance distortions or omissions by use of other material, or by specifically pointing out implicit assumptions and using them as discussion points. Look, for example, for the range of family groupings or relationships portrayed. Are individuals from black and ethnic minority groups included? Are individuals with disabilities shown in a positive light? Is it age-appropriate for the student or group you are working with?

In summary, get support for yourself. Know your students well. Be clear what you are teaching and why. Familiarise yourself with any resource you use. Be prepared to be flexible and to treat resources not so much as a magic answer but more like the curate's egg – good in parts.

References

1 Craft, A. (ed.) (1987). Mental handicap and sexuality: issues for individuals with a mental handicap, their parents and professionals, *Mental handicap and sexuality: issues and perspectives.* Tunbridge Wells: Costello.

2 Scott, L. and the Image in Action Team (1994). *On the agenda: sex education for young people with learning difficulties.* Image in Action, Jackson's Lane Community Centre, Archway Road, London N6 5AA.

3 Craft, A. and Downs, C. (1997). *Sex in Context.* Brighton, Pavilion Publishing Ltd.

Topics index

Access to health services (includes complaints and involvement in service provision)

Access to community care services (includes complaints and involvement in service provision)

Advocacy (includes self-advocacy)

Alcohol

Child health (physical)

Communication (includes language development, translation, interpreting, ESOL materials, and specific communication disorders)

Death and dying (includes bereavement and grief counselling)

Drugs and solvent misuse

Education (includes schools and adult learning)

Environment (includes living conditions)

Equal opportunities

Food hygiene (i.e. food safety)

Health conditions and illnesses

Inter-personal and social skills (includes communication and life-skills)

Leisure (includes arts, crafts, drama, play)

Living in the community

Mental health (includes well-being, emotional resilience, and specific mental illnesses)

Nutrition (includes diet and healthy eating)

Oral health

Parenting (includes family issues)

Physical activity (includes movement and sport)

Physical disability

Physical, sexual, and emotional abuse

Professional development

Safety (includes accident prevention and personal safety)

Sexual health and personal relationships (includes contraception, STDs, HIV/AIDS, sexuality and personal relationships)

Smoking

Work and the workplace

Format index

Audio cassettes

Books and booklets

Card, photo, slide, picture block sets, stickers

Multimedia

Packs

Videos and video packs

Resources

Able autistic children: children with Asperger's syndrome: a booklet for brothers and sisters

FORMAT: Booklet, 23-pages, illustrated
AUDIENCE: Brothers and sisters from 7 years upwards, parents
PRICE: £2.50 + p&p
PRODUCER: Nottingham: University of Nottingham, 1994
DISTRIBUTOR: The National Autistic Society

This booklet was developed following work with a support group for brothers and sisters of children with autism. It aims to help children understand able autism, Asperger's syndrome, and provide relevant terms and explanations. It is intended for use by children aged seven or over with adult support. The booklet is divided into sections that explain what able autism means, describe the sorts of difficulties able autistic children have, suggest ways to explain autism to other people who don't know about it, raise some of the things the reader might find difficult as a brother or sister, and share some of the good things about being a brother or sister.

The explanations and examples are clear, relevant to children and use accessible language – for example, describing difficulties in taking turns or seeing things from someone else's point of view. Text is accompanied by black-and-white line drawings of family situations. The booklet uses a question and answer format to explore issues such as: Will he ever get better?; Why does he want to be on his own a lot?; Why won't he play with me?; Why won't he join in our games?; Why does he ignore me sometimes?; and Why can't he keep secrets? The booklet suggests answers to all these questions, and also invites the reader to offer her or his own answers. The section on explaining to others looks at the situations in which the reader might need or want to talk about autism, and offers actual phrases she or he could use.

Other areas covered include difficult times, which looks at being treated differently by parents and conflicting feelings towards a brother or sister with autism. It explores issues that might arise from being an older or younger sibling – for example, having to be especially responsible. This section may help to validate the conflicting feelings brothers and sisters may have and quotes children speaking about a range of things they have found difficult. The booklet also includes a section about what children liked about having a brother or sister with autism, quoting for example a 10-year-old saying, 'I'm usually good at working out what he's saying'. It concludes with pages for the reader to fill in, prompted by headings such as 'The things you would like to change to make things better for you are ...'

The resource focuses on the challenges and positive aspects of family life with a child with able autism. It could be used by individual children (with an adult) or in sibling support groups. The use of quotes from other children will be a valuable trigger for readers to offer their own experiences. The author has written a second book in this series entitled *Children with autism – a book for brothers and sisters*, which uses a similar format.

Advocacy of love: part of our lives

FORMAT: Video, 10 mins
AUDIENCE: People with learning disabilities
AUTHOR: Swindon People First
PRICE: £15.00 + p&p
PRODUCER: Swindon: Thamesdown Borough Council Media Arts Unit, 1996
DISTRIBUTOR: Swindon People First
This documentary video was devised by members of Swindon People First, a group of adults with learning disabilities. It explores people's experiences and feelings about love and friendship. The video covers all forms of love, including friends, family, lovers, pets, and food. It is well produced with professional support and consists mainly of members of the group speaking to camera and to each other, against a black backdrop. This is interspersed with visuals of group members doing dance and movement and reaching out to one another.
The group describe their own experiences – what love means to them and what love does. They speak about the joy and pain love can bring, the hurt caused by lack of love, and the part love and friendship play in dealing with problems. The group includes people from black and minority ethnic groups and people with physical disabilities. Group members sing songs that are important to them and tell jokes. The overall atmosphere of the video is one of intimacy, of a group that has built up a lot of trust and has come to be very open with each other.
The video is a good example of what is involved when a group explores a particular theme. It would be useful to show to a group embarking on a similar project. It shows people with learning disabilities experiencing the ordinary joys and sorrows of love and could be shown in the training of supporters, staff, and others who work with people with learning disabilities to increase their understanding. It could also be used in schools as part of a project to counter prejudice. The video does not deal in depth with sexual love, or with the experience of rejection familiar to many people with learning disabilities, but it could act as a trigger for a group to discuss how love affects them. There are no accompanying notes.

At home with self-advocacy

FORMAT: Booklet, 18-pages, illustrated
AUDIENCE: Carers
PRICE: £1.50 inc.
PRODUCER: Nottingham: EMFEC, 1994
DISTRIBUTOR: EMFEC

This booklet is a guide to self-advocacy for carers of people with learning disabilities. This could include family, friends, or others involved in their lives. It is a good introduction for those unfamiliar with the concept of self-advocacy.

The authors set out to define clearly what self-advocacy is, why it is important for people with a learning disability, and the carer's role in this. There is a section about actively encouraging self-advocacy, particularly in relation to service providers, which talks about some of the very positive benefits for the individual concerned. It also touches briefly on some of the common problems that can arise.
The booklet suggests ways in which carers can increase their own self-advocacy skills and also look for support. It stresses the need to consider the conflicts of interest that might arise for them and suggests that finding independent support might be of greater benefit to the person they care for. There are humorous black-and-white cartoon illustrations and a further information section including selected reading, useful resources, and addresses. Both the print and the drawings are fairly small and might not be suitable for someone with sight difficulties.
No reference is made to cultural differences and whether this might affect self-advocacy. It is one of a series of publications about self-advocacy and was funded by the Department of Health.

Autism: behind an invisible wall

FORMAT: Video pack – video 23 mins; notes, 8-pages
AUDIENCE: Young people without disabilities or with moderate learning disabilities, teachers
AUTHOR: Jones, E.
PRICE: £12.99 + p&p
PRODUCER: London: The National Autistic Society, 1994
DISTRIBUTOR: The National Autistic Society
This video is produced by the National Autistic Society and aims to foster understanding of people with autism, encourage discussion of attitudes, and focus attention on human relationships and on communication. It is narrated by actress Jane Asher and shows young people at Helen Allison and Radlett Lodge schools for autistic children in the playground and at lessons. The video stresses that autistic children have difficulty communicating and relating to others and can exhibit obsessive behaviour.
It is intended for use in school classrooms as a focus for discussion and is accompanied by notes for facilitators. The booklet suggests that young people explore their own networks of relationships prior to viewing the video and relate this to the difficulties experienced by the children in the video. The notes stress the importance of the facilitator previewing the video before use.
Primarily, this video is aimed at young people without disabilities. However, sections of the video could be used with young people or adults with moderate learning disabilities to trigger discussion about attitudes towards disability. The booklet includes a list of books and pamphlets available from the National Autistic Society.

The big sex show – video

FORMAT: Video pack – video 34 mins; booklets (x3), 10-pages, 16-pages, 12-pages
AUDIENCE: 16+ years with mild to moderate learning disabilities
AUTHOR: The Lawnmowers
PRICE: £25.00 + p&p (video only); £7.50 + p&p (booklets)
PRODUCER: Newcastle upon Tyne: Swingbridge Video, 1995
DISTRIBUTOR: Them Wifies
This pack is aimed at people aged 16 years and over who have mild to moderate learning disabilities. It consists of a video and three booklets and sets out to explain

some of the problems people may experience when relationships begin and people become closer.

This video features the Lawnmowers, a theatre company of people with learning disabilities. The actors explain the parts they are going to play, and the action takes place between a group of friends who go to a day centre. It follows the relationships that develop.

The dialogue is humorous and the language uncomplicated. The video explains that it is important to understand the facts, and the feelings and fears attached to relationships are discussed. Issues raised include homosexuality, privacy, and problems around parental control. Anxieties about visiting a family planning clinic for the first time may be dispelled, as are some of the popular myths about HIV/AIDS. There is no reference to other sexually transmitted diseases or sexual hygiene.

The booklets reflect the themes of the video and include more information and details about where to go for help. There are black-and-white illustrations and a clear text. The booklet, *Sex, meeting people and condoms*, also includes a worksheet.

This video pack could be used as part of a planned course and is suitable for viewing in informal settings and by small groups or individuals. There is no one from a black or minority ethnic group involved in this production and the pack might have limited use for people with sight difficulties. The project was funded by the South Tyne Health Commission and is a 'Them Wifies' project.

Bob tells all

FORMAT: Book, 62-pages, illustrated
AUDIENCE: Men with learning disabilities who have been abused, support workers, carers
AUTHOR: Hollins, S., Sinason, V., and Webb, B. (illustrator)
PRICE: £10.00 inc.
PRODUCER: London: St George's Hospital Medical School, 1993
DISTRIBUTOR: Royal College of Psychiatrists, Book Sales
ISBN: 1 874439 03 6

This colour picture book was written by a psychiatrist and a psychotherapist and is one of the *Books beyond words* series for people with learning disabilities. It is designed for men with a learning disability who have been sexually abused and who need an opportunity to talk about their experiences. The book contains colour illustrations and on each facing page there are between one and three short sentences in large print. It tells the story of Bob who, with the help of a social worker, is able to tell about being sexually abused.

The story begins with Bob moving into a group home and making friends with his new house-mates. That night, he wakes everyone in the house with his screaming, and in the morning he is very upset. He becomes aggressive towards one of the people he lives with and smashes things up. Bob's social worker is called and is able to help Bob talk about what is worrying him. Bob tells him about a man who used to abuse him at night in the place where he used to live. The social worker is sympathetic and explains to Bob's house-mates that Bob has been badly treated. Bob apologises for his behaviour and all of them are able to relax in each other's company again. The social worker tells Bob that they have lots more talking to do.

The book could be used by someone alone who had limited reading skills or could be read with someone. The pictures are very powerful, and facial expressions and colour vividly convey feelings. It could be used by people with severe learning disabilities, as the visual imagery is so clear – there are no distracting details, just strong colour and expressive body language. A sentence of text accompanies each picture, giving scope for readers to discuss each image and tell the story in their own words.

The book should be used sensitively, and before use the parent, carer, or teacher will need to prepare the reader as well as planning follow-up work. It could prompt a revelation of sexual abuse, so those using the book should have the expertise to deal with this and have access to a support network. There is also a laminated loose-leaf version available. Another book in the series, *Jenny speaks out* (1992), tells the story of a woman who has been sexually abused.

Brothers, sisters and learning disability: a guide for parents

FORMAT: Booklet, 21-pages, illustrated
AUDIENCE: Parents and families
AUTHOR: Tozer, R.
PRICE: £5.00 inc.
PRODUCER: Kidderminster: British Institute of Learning Disabilities (BILD), 1996
DISTRIBUTOR: BILD Publications, Plymbridge Distributors
ISBN: 1873791879

This A5 booklet is intended for families who have a child with a learning disability. Written by a parent of two children with learning and other disabilities, this booklet examines the impact of a child with a learning disability on other children in the family and considers what parents can do to encourage acceptance and understanding. It also aims to address parents' anxieties about how the other children are coping with what they might feel is an unusual family life.

Descriptions are given of common events and experiences in the lives of brothers and sisters of people with learning disabilities, and ideas are provided about how to ease difficult situations. It consists of text and some black-and-white line drawings showing family situations. Separate from the main text, examples are given of solutions parents have found to common problems, together with quotes from both children and adults.

A theme running through the booklet is the importance of talking. It looks at how children come to understand disability. If brothers and sisters are not provided with explanations and information they can understand, they may invent their own. For example, it suggests older children (of about nine or ten) often experience a period of grief about their sibling's disability of which parents may not be aware. It suggests that parents listen to their children's behaviour as well as to their words. The booklet touches upon the skills brothers and sisters may gain – for example, in playing with children with learning disabilities on their own terms. It also looks at the mixed feelings children may have and recommends that they shouldn't always feel that they have to entertain or give in to their sibling. It stresses the importance of allowing some privacy for each child in the family. One section explores the emotions in the family when a child dies.

The last part of the booklet looks at the world outside, briefly covering bullying and the need of adolescents for independence. It would be useful to parents, grandparents, and other relatives, as well as people who work with families and want to learn more about how children may respond to a brother or sister with a learning disability. A list of books and contacts for further information is also provided.

Building friendships – a resource pack to help young people make friendships and develop relationships

FORMAT: Pack, 192-pages, illustrated
AUDIENCE: Young people of varying abilities
AUTHORS: Firth, H., Fraser, J., Nelson, P., and Mayor, J.
PRICE: £35.00 inc.
PRODUCER: London: Brook Advisory Centres, 1994
DISTRIBUTOR: London: Brook Advisory Centres
ISBN: 0 946168 04 0
This resource pack contains a wide range of ideas for facilitating work with young people who may experience difficulties in making friends. Facilitators can use the exercises as they are given or select parts and use them as a basis for their own session plans. A wide variety of teaching methods is used, including role play, using pictures, lists, questionnaires, action plans and stories, ideas for using video and soap operas, and more. The stories include some black-and-white line drawings as storyboards, showing people of different ages and ethnic groups meeting in a variety of settings. The pack also gives guidance to facilitators about ways of implementing and evaluating the work. It encourages pre-planning and a commitment to looking at ways of providing real opportunities for participants to meet others.
Subject areas covered include: icebreakers and getting to know each other games; meeting people and getting to know them better; social skills; building friendships through doing things together; helping others to get to know each other; dealing with risk and hurt feelings; close friendships; and personal safety. Love and sex is mentioned within the context of friendship but not looked at in any detail. Those wishing to move on to sex education will need to use other resources.
The resource is versatile and could be adapted for use with people of varying abilities and ages. Worksheets, which can be photocopied easily, use symbols, words, and pictures. For example, one worksheet uses a cartoon face in each of four boxes with a line of text: 'One thing I want to do is'; 'One thing I like doing is'; 'Another thing I need help with is'; and 'Another thing I'm good at is'. The session plans are easy to follow with clearly laid out aims and methods.

Building social networks

FORMAT: Pack - video, 50 mins; A4 ring-binder training notes, 36-pages; photocopiable worksheets, 9-pages; OHP transparencies (x2)
AUDIENCE: Young people and adults with moderate learning disabilities, support workers, carers
AUTHORS: Brown, H. and Brown, V.
PRICE: £146.88 inc. + 10% p&p
PRODUCER: Canterbury: The Tizard Centre
DISTRIBUTOR: Pavilion Publishing Ltd.
ISBN: 1 871080 62 2
This resource is an update and re-issue of one of the original *Bringing people back home* series of video training packs. It contains a 50-minute video and an A4 folder, which includes planned sessions, instructions on how to use the video, and additional training materials. It is primarily a resource for professional development and is intended to be used in workshop situations.
The video shows how a group of people with severe learning disabilities and physical disabilities have built up social networks after moving from hospital into a small group home. It looks at how people make social contacts, how staff can actively

increase opportunities for the residents, and how people who may not have come into contact with people with disabilities can be supported. Initiatives include one resident attending a youth club and other residents' relationships with befrienders and support workers. The pack stresses the differences between the roles of a paid worker and a friend. It is based on the principles of normalisation.

The video is divided into five sections: People in our lives; Meeting people; Paving the way; Who does what; and Conclusion. The supplementary materials could be useful for direct use with people with learning disabilities. These include: a Circle of friends chart that looks at who an individual comes into contact with; Meeting people, which looks at how to increase the opportunities for meeting people; and Paving the way, which helps you decide what information should be given to people meeting a person with learning disabilities for the first time. Who does what sheets identify who is the appropriate person to help achieve objectives.

While the pack is specifically designed to help workers to improve opportunities for people with severe learning disabilities, the supporting materials mentioned could usefully be used with young people and adults with moderate learning disabilities to stimulate discussion about friendship and privacy.

But now they've got a voice

FORMAT: Cassette, 31mins; notes, 33-pages
AUDIENCE: Adults with learning disabilities who have been abused, support workers, carers
AUTHOR: Brown, H. and Stein, J. (eds.)
PRICE: £15.95 + VAT + p&p
PRODUCER: Canterbury: The Tizard Centre, 1996
DISTRIBUTOR: Pavilion Publishing Ltd
ISBN: 1871080940

This resource consists of an audio cassette, made by people with learning disabilities who are survivors of sexual abuse, and a booklet. It was made as part of a five-year programme of work at the Tizard Centre, University of Kent on the sexual abuse of adults with learning disabilities.

The cassette includes interviews and group discussions in which survivors tell their stories and reflect on their experiences.

The tape is divided into three sections. Section 1, What is sexual abuse?, includes survivors' views of sexual abuse, looking at people's rights to give and withhold their consent to sexual relationships or acts. It makes clear that people who abuse are usually known to the person abused rather than strangers, and that this can include people in powerful positions such as staff or family members.

Section 2, Finding someone you can tell, may help people to review their own experiences and comment on things that they have not liked. It gives a strong message that abuse is the fault of the abuser, not the person who has been abused, and encourages people not to keep the abuse a secret.

Section 3, Getting help, looks at what might happen when someone discloses abuse. It includes an interview with a police officer about the action the police can take to support people with learning disabilities. The people on the tape describe the long-term effects of having been abused and share what has helped them to recover. One woman had counselling which helped her to deal with flashbacks, and another joined a women's group and took part in a number of activities to help other women feel safe. The tape ends by encouraging people to get help and affirming that they can get support in dealing with the aftermath of abuse.

The booklet contains a transcript of the cassette and notes for facilitators. The notes suggest the tape could be used in sex education groups, or women's or men's groups, or with an individual who has been sexually abused. It emphasises that it should be used alongside preparation and support – for example, enabling listeners to become comfortable with using sexual words and exploring issues such as consent, before hearing the tape. It suggests that people should listen with support and that facilitators should consider in advance what they will do if a member discloses sexual abuse that has happened to them. The booklet also contains a summary of the tape's contents and lists of useful addresses and books.

Made during a weekend workshop, the sound quality on the tape is poor, but the energy of the event as survivors come together to talk to each other comes through powerfully. The group wanted to use what had happened to them to help other people with learning disabilities. The tape should be a support to those who have experienced abuse and a means of educating others who might be at risk.

Chance to choose

FORMAT: Pack, 129-pages, illustrated
AUDIENCE: Young people 11+ years with learning disabilities
AUTHOR: Dixon, H.
PRICE: £17.00 + VAT, with surcharge of £3.95 for orders under £70.00
PRODUCER: Cambridge: Learning Development Aids, 1994
DISTRIBUTOR: Learning Development Aids

This pack, a new edition of *Sexuality and mental handicap*, contains tried and tested practical ideas for approaching sex education with people with learning disabilities. It covers eight broad topic areas: body awareness; self-esteem; communication; relationships; looking after me; being sexual; pregnancy; birth and parenting; and sexual health. A series of participatory group activities is suggested for each which encourage exploration of feelings and values as well as discussion of information. Little equipment is required for these activities and each topic heading includes a list of suggested resources that can be used as supporting material.

Intended for young people aged 11 years and upwards, the activities can be adapted easily to meet the needs of different age groups. Although they require participants to have verbal skills, these activities can also be adapted for people using sign language or with limited communication skills. They could be used on a one-to-one basis rather than with a group. 'Picture yourself', a pack of four sets of cards containing line drawings and photos, has been published by Learning Development Aids to accompany this book. Some suggestions are provided about sex education generally, but no help is offered with difficulties that may be experienced in groups, nor does it suggest how to evaluate activities. Some supplementary material would be required in dealing with issues of HIV and safer sex, as there is only one activity about this entitled 'AIDS: what I need to know', which involves concepts of 'high', 'low', and 'no' risk. There are some activities about sexually transmitted diseases. The pack is an excellent base upon which to build a sex education programme.

Children need healthy food

FORMAT: Booklet, 10-pages, illustrated
AUDIENCE: Parents with learning disabilities
AUTHOR: McGaw, S.
PRICE: £10.00 + p&p
PRODUCER: Kidderminster: British Institute of Learning Disabilities (BILD), 1995
DISTRIBUTOR: BILD Publications, Plymbridge Distributors
ISBN: 1873791410;
ISBN: 1873791313 Series

This is the second booklet in the *I want to be a good parent* series and provides information for parents with learning disabilities about feeding children from 0–2 years. The five titles were written by Sue McGaw of the Special Parenting Service, which works with parents with learning disabilities. The aim of the series as a whole is to identify, simplify, and teach the skills needed to be a parent. The booklets are aimed at parents or prospective parents with learning disabilities.

Children need healthy food is a 10-page booklet with colour illustrations of parents and children from a range of ethnic groups. It covers the various kinds of food children need at different ages: 0–3 months; 4–5 months; 6–8 months; 9–12 months; 1–2 years; and 2 years and older. There is information about breast-feeding and bottle feeding, and suggestions for foods to try and those that should not be given.

The advice given is easy to follow because the main ideas are conveyed through the pictures. Those with reading skills will be able to use the booklet independently. In most cases, it will be helpful if a friend or facilitator discusses the contents of the booklet with the parent with a learning disability first – perhaps only using those pages that are relevant to the current age of their child or children. Some non-readers who have looked at it several times with a facilitator may find they are able to use the picture alone to remind them of the main points. The booklet can also be used to support and re-inforce advice and discussions with health professionals and others. It is also appropriate for use in group settings to promote discussion of parenting.

Other books in the series are: *What's it like to be a parent?*; *Children need to be clean, healthy and warm*; *Children need to be safe*; and *Children need love.*

Children need love

FORMAT: Booklet, 7-pages, illustrated
AUDIENCE: Parents with learning disabilities
AUTHOR: McGaw, S.
PRICE: £10.00 + p&p
PRODUCER: Kidderminster: British Institute of Learning Disabilities (BILD), 1995
DISTRIBUTOR: BILD Publications, Plymbridge Distributors
ISBN: 1873791569;
ISBN: 1873791313 Series

This is the fifth booklet in the *I want to be a good parent* series. It provides information for parents with learning disabilities about showing children affection and teaching good behaviour. The five titles are written by Sue McGaw of the Special Parenting Service, which works with parents with learning disabilities. The aim of the series as a whole is to identify, simplify, and teach the skills needed to be a parent. These booklets are aimed at parents or prospective parents with learning disabilities and could also be useful to people with learning disabilities who work with or share a home with children.

Children need love is a seven-page A4 booklet with colour illustrations of parents and children from a range of ethnic groups. The text is brief and the pictures tell much of what is being described. The booklet looks at ways of showing love and affection – for example, it shows parents teaching their children to do things and teaching them right from wrong. There is a drawing of a child painting a picture and getting paint over himself. Two mothers are watching; one is thinking 'He is very quiet – what a lovely picture!', the other is thinking 'Look at the mess – he is such a bad boy!' Readers are asked to consider which mother they agree with. The booklet suggests that he is quiet and learning to paint so why not leave him? Better still, join him and have fun painting. Further examples show different ways of teaching right from wrong, including teaching children to be safe, to make friends, and to eat healthy food and telling them why they should behave properly. Two pages look at understanding and managing behaviour, exploring, for example: 'What do you do when he is difficult? Does he get lots of attention when this happens and not much when he is good? Try spending more time with him when he behaves well'.

The advice given is easy to follow because the main ideas are conveyed through the pictures. Those with reading skills will be able to use the booklet independently. Some non-readers who have looked at it several times with a facilitator may find they are able to use the pictures alone to remind them of the main points. The booklet can also be used to support and re-inforce advice and discussions with health professionals and others. It is also appropriate for use in group settings to promote discussion of parenting.

Other booklets in the series are: *What's it like to be a parent?*; *Children need healthy food*; *Children need to be clean, healthy and warm*; and *Children need to be safe.*

Children need to be clean, healthy and warm

FORMAT: Booklet, 9-pages, illustrated
AUDIENCE: Parents with learning disabilities
AUTHOR: McGaw, S.
PRICE: £10.00 + p&p
PRODUCER: Kidderminster: British Institute for Learning Disabilities (BILD), 1995
DISTRIBUTOR: BILD Publications, Plymbridge Distributors.
ISBN: 1873791461;
ISBN: 1873791313 Series

This is the third booklet in the *I want to be a good parent* series, providing information for parents with learning disabilities about keeping children clean, healthy, and warm. The five titles were written by Sue McGaw of the Special Parenting Service, which works with parents with learning disabilities. The aim of the series as a whole is to identify, simplify, and teach the skills needed to be a parent. The booklets are aimed at parents or prospective parents with learning disabilities.

Children need to be clean, healthy and warm is a nine-page booklet with colour illustrations that show parents and children from a range of ethnic groups. It covers the reasons why children need to be clean, explaining for example that children can get tummy bugs and will be sick if they have dirty bodies, teaching children to wash their hands after going to the toilet and before eating, frequent bathing and washing, taking children for check-ups, inoculations, and dental and other health check-ups. It also looks at keeping clothes and shoes clean and fitting the child with appropriate clothing for different seasons, making sure children are warm but not too hot in bed – for example, removing hot water bottles and switching off electric blankets before they get in – and keeping the house clean and warm with a supply of fresh food.

The advice given is easy to follow because the main ideas are conveyed through the pictures. Those with reading skills will be able to use the booklet independently. In most cases, it will be helpful if a friend or facilitator discusses the contents of the booklet with the parent with a learning disability first. Some non-readers who have looked at it several times with a facilitator may find they are able to use the pictures alone to remind them of the main points. The booklet can also be used to support and re-inforce advice and discussions with health professionals and others. It is also appropriate for use in group settings to promote discussion of parenting.

Other booklets in the series are: *What's it like to be a parent?*; *Children need healthy food*; *Children need to be safe*; and *Children need love*.

Children need to be safe

FORMAT: Booklet, 11-pages, illustrated
AUDIENCE: Parents with learning disabilities
AUTHOR: McGaw, S.
PRICE: £10.00 + p&p
PRODUCER: Kidderminster: British Institute for Learning Disabilities (BILD), 1995
DISTRIBUTOR: BILD Publications, Plymbridge Distributors.
ISBN: 1873791518;
ISBN: 1873791313 Series

This is the fourth booklet in the *I want to be a good parent* series providing information for parents with learning disabilities about making a home safe for children. The five titles were written by Sue McGaw of the Special Parenting Service, which works with parents with learning disabilities. The aim of the series as a whole is to identify, simplify, and teach the skills needed to be a parent. These booklets are aimed at parents or prospective parents with learning disabilities and might also be useful to people with learning disabilities who work with or share a home with children.

Children need to be safe is an 11-page booklet with colour illustrations that show parents and children from a range of ethnic groups. The text is brief and the pictures tell much of what is being described. It looks at the danger of burns or scalds, fire prevention, choking and suffocating, cot death, the danger of falls, and the danger of cuts from sharp objects, poisons, drowning, electricity and gas, and roads and cars. For example, one page gives information about dealing with an accident or emergency when the child is very ill. It includes a list of emergency situations along with instructions for calling the doctor or an ambulance. The text is brief and broken into short sections illustrated with pictures; for example, 'Medicines – Lock away. Use child proof tops'. Readers are encouraged to respond to the situations it explores; for example, there are two 'spot the dangers' pictures: one titled 'Danger of Burns or Scalds' and the other 'Danger from Fire, Electricity and Gas'. Elsewhere, a mini story shows a mother giving her toddler a bath when the door bell rings. It asks 'What should the Mum do?' and gives the answer 'Let the doorbell ring or take your child with you.'

On the last page of the booklet there are suggestions for further reading, wall charts, First Aid training, and brief information about special needs services that may be available from electricity offices.

The advice given is easy to follow because the main ideas are conveyed through the pictures. Those with reading skills will be able to use the booklet independently. In most cases, it will be helpful if a friend or facilitator discusses the contents of the booklet with the parent with a learning disability first. Some non-readers who have looked at it several times with a facilitator may find they are able to use the pictures alone to remind them of the main points. The booklet can also be used to support and reinforce advice and discussions with health professionals and others. It is also appropriate for use in group settings to promote discussion of parenting. Although intended for parents with learning disabilities, the booklet might also be useful to teach older children about some of the potential hazards to avoid.

Other booklets in the series are: *What's it like to be a parent?*; *Children need healthy food*; *Children need to be clean, healthy and warm*; and *Children need love.*

Choices

FORMAT: Videos (x3)
AUDIENCE: People with learning disabilities
PRICE: £70 inc.; £55 inc. for advocacy groups
PRODUCER: Rotherham: Speakup Self Advocacy
DISTRIBUTOR: Speakup Self Advocacy

Choices is a series of videos produced by Speakup, a self-advocacy group in Rotherham. The aim is to give people who cannot read information about various issues that affect their lives and the choices they can make. The three videos, *How to have fun*, *Where can I live?*, *What can I do in the day?*, are reviewed individually.

Choices: fun things to do

FORMAT: Video, 15 mins
AUDIENCE: People with learning disabilities
PRICE: £25.00 single video or £55.00 Choices videos x3 (advocacy groups); £28.00 single video or £70.00 Choices videos x3 (other groups)
PRODUCER: Rotherham: Speakup Self Advocacy, 1995
DISTRIBUTOR: Speakup Self Advocacy
Fun things to do introduces a range of leisure activities and includes sections on leisure centres, country parks, pubs, Gateway clubs, going to the theatre and cinema, shopping, visiting museums, and outdoor activities. The sections are brief and show people with learning disabilities doing things for themselves, enjoying each other's company and having fun. In the first section, At the leisure centre, we see Gladys paying for and then playing a game of badminton at her local leisure centre, and then going into the learner's swimming pool. The final section, Outdoor activities, shows disabled people learning canoeing, playing football, and using an artificial climbing slope. Each situation is shown with a minimum of editing and at a gentle pace which allows the viewer time to absorb and think about whether that particular option is right for them.
The video would be useful for individuals or groups to explore the leisure options available to them and to help them make decisions about what they could do and how they might set about doing it. The activities shown, though local to Rotherham, are varied enough to be relevant to most areas. Facilitators or groups using the video might need to gather information about local leisure facilities before using the video to make sure the choices it offers exist in their area. The video would be particularly useful in helping people think about what new activities they might enjoy and what support they might need to do them.
There is a leaflet to go with the videos and this reminds the reader, 'You only live once ... so the choices you make are important to you'. It describes briefly why the videos have been made and how they can be used. The back of the leaflet has space for people to write down phone numbers of people and places who can offer further information and support in making choices.

Choices: what can I do during the day?

FORMAT: Video, 15 mins
AUDIENCE: People with learning disabilities
PRICE: £25.00 single video or £55.00 Choices videos x3 (advocacy groups); £28.00 single video or £70.00 Choices videos x3 (other groups)
PRODUCER: Rotherham: Speakup Self Advocacy, 1995
DISTRIBUTOR: Speakup Self Advocacy
What can I do during the day? introduces a wide range of options for people with learning disabilities to do during the day. Made and presented by people with learning disabilities, it shows a series of different activities and venues accompanied by a voice-over giving additional information.
The video includes sections on day centres, community resources, clubs, work experience, one-off sessions, courses, drama groups, and libraries. The final section is about self-expression and shows people talking individually to camera about the activities they like.
Each section sets out to show visually a number of possible activities, from the conventional to the more

imaginative. The section on day centres, for example, shows a cooking session, someone receiving a massage, a discussion group, a project collecting cans for South Africa, and an individual hobby – stamp collecting. The video also touches on the skills and support services that enable people with learning disabilities to live independently.

The section on courses shows a going out course, with people involved in group and one-to-one discussions with workers planning the things they need to do, such as prepare a packed lunch. It then shows the group using public transport and a café, putting into action what they have learned. The section on employment suggests working with a Pathway officer to find a work placement. It then shows people with learning disabilities working as packers and caterers for well-known firms. The activities are portrayed with a minimum of editing and at a gentle pace which allows the viewer time to absorb and think about whether that particular option is right for them.

The video would be useful for individuals or groups to explore the choices available to them and to help make decisions about how they spend their day. It could be watched alone or with a support worker. The activities shown are varied enough to be relevant to any town, though some may not be available in rural areas. Facilitators or groups using the video might need to gather information about local activities before using the video to make sure the choices it offers exist in their area.

There is a leaflet to go with the videos and this reminds the reader, 'You only live once ... so the choices you make are important to you'. It describes briefly why the videos have been made and how they can be used. The back of the leaflet has space for people to write down phone numbers of people and places who can offer further information and support in making choices.

Choices: where can I live?

FORMAT: Video, 15 mins
AUDIENCE: People with learning disabilities
PRICE: £25.00 single video or £55.00 Choices videos x3 (advocacy groups); £28.00 single video or £70.00 Choices videos x3 (other groups)
PRODUCER: Rotherham: Speakup Self Advocacy, 1995
DISTRIBUTOR: Speakup Self Advocacy

Where can I live? introduces a range of housing options to viewers. Made and presented by people with learning disabilities, it shows a range of different living situations and describes how they have been made possible. A voice-over provides additional information.

The video includes sections on group homes, resource centres, family life, living with a landlady, private accommodation, residential units, nursing homes, Mencap homes, and living with friends. The sections are brief and most show people with learning disabilities living independently and doing things for themselves. In the section on group homes, we see residents washing up, hoovering, and hanging out washing. In another home a young man describes the support he gets from workers and then shows us around his house. The section on family life shows a woman with a learning disability living with her husband and two children in their home. The video touches on the skills and support that may be needed in each situation. In the section on resource centres, a woman who is preparing to live on her own is shown learning to cook meals for herself.

The video also focuses on the social dimension of housing choices, being able to choose who you live with and who you invite into your home. In the section on nursing homes a resident is shown inviting a friend in for a cup of tea. The final section, Living with friends, shows Peter, whose parents have died, living in their bungalow with friends, with the aid of a support worker. The voice-over tells how this was arranged by social services. Each situation is shown with a minimum of editing and at a gentle pace, which allows the viewer time to absorb and think about whether that particular option is right for them.

The video would be useful for individuals or groups to explore the housing choices available to them and to help them make decisions about how and where they could live. The housing situations shown are varied enough to be relevant to any town, though some may not be available in rural areas. Facilitators or groups using the video might need to gather information about local housing options before using the video to make sure the choices it offers exist in their area. The video would be particularly useful in helping people think about the support they might need in order to live in the way they want to and enabling them to assess their own strengths and skills.

There is a leaflet to go with the videos and this reminds the reader, 'You only live once ... so the choices you make are important to you'. It describes briefly why the videos were made and how they can be used. The back of the leaflet has space for people to write down phone numbers of people and places who can offer further information and support in making choices.

Circles – intimacy and relationships

FORMAT: Pack – videos (x12); handbook, 105-pages; laminated A4 cards; stickers; PVC mat
AUDIENCE: People with learning disabilities
AUTHORS: Champagne, M. and Walker-Hirsch, L.
PRICE: US$599.00 each + p&p + customs charges
PRODUCER: Santa Barbara: James Stanfield Co. Inc., 1993 (revised edition)
DISTRIBUTOR: James Stanfield Co. Inc., USA

Using short, easy-to-locate videos and step-by-step session plans, this resource uses the concept of differently coloured concentric circles emanating from an individual to convey the idea of different types of relationship. The central circle, 'the purple private circle', represents each of us as individuals; the second circle, 'the blue hug circle', contains those people who are close to us – possibly immediate family members and partners. 'The green faraway hug circle' represents those people we know well but not as well as close family, and so on.

The resource is divided into two main parts – relationships and relationship building. In the first six videos the presenter, a young white American woman, interacts with various people, from her parents and brother in her 'blue hug circle' to a teacher at college in the 'yellow handshake circle' and a complete stranger she sees in the local shop – in the 'red stranger space'. She explains the differences in each of these relationships and describes appropriate behaviour in each situation. For example, she might hug a close family member and tell them about her feelings, but this would not be appropriate with someone she knows less well, such as someone in the 'yellow handshake circle'. One of the videos gives a summary to recap this idea of different types of relationship.

The second part of the resource looks at building relationships and includes a further six videos that look at ways in which relationships might change. One example is the young woman's boyfriend. We see that at first she didn't know him at all. Through a number of different situations she gradually gets to know him as an acquaintance, then as a friend, and finally they decide to become partners. Another example shows some neighbours whom she doesn't know when they first move in, but gets to know well enough to smile and wave to.

There is a series of clearly presented session plans to accompany the videos. These guide people through each stage and encourage them to use the circles system to understand better the different relationships in their life and appropriate behaviour within those different relationships. Circle diagrams are provided for people to colour and complete with names or pictures of the people they know. A large PVC mat is provided with the coloured circles printed on it which can be used as a wall chart on which photographs can be stuck, or as a floor mat on which people could stand and perhaps act out some different interactions – hugs, handshakes, waves, and so on. Users of the resource are invited to share stories about people they have got to know and friendships that have developed. Many people with learning disabilities do not have the same opportunity to make new friends and pursue romantic relationships as others and many will not live with two parents and siblings as the woman in the video does. Therefore, facilitators may want to use supplementary materials to represent a range of possible relationships.

A third section in the handbook, which is not accompanied by videos, looks at topics in sex education – self-esteem, personal hygiene, feelings, puberty, masturbation, dating, marriage, sex, conception, and parenting. These subjects are not covered in detail but the handbook gives ideas for discussion and outlines ways in which sex education can be related to the Circles programme. Readers are referred to other more comprehensive sex education resources such as the Life Horizons series. There is no mention of gay or lesbian relationships.

This material could be used to introduce discussions about families and relationships, either before moving on to fuller sex education or as part of a sex education programme. The videos are in an American format (NTSC) and there may be an extra charge for making UK compatible (PAL) copies.

ColorCards: basic sequences

FORMAT: Boxed card-set – A5 cards (x48), colour; notes, 4-pages
AUDIENCE: Children and adults with learning disabilities
PRICE: £23.75 + VAT + 12% p&p
PRODUCER: Bicester: Winslow Press, 1994
DISTRIBUTOR: Winslow Press

This sequencing ColorCard pack was designed for use with a wide range of ages and disabilities where there is a need to develop language and other associated skills. An effective aid for working with learning disabled adults and children, the pack is relatively simple to use and has a clear instruction leaflet enclosed.

The pack consists of 48 durable colour photographs arranged in three-step sequences. These depict people engaged in every-day activities – for example, eating, drinking, writing, sewing, playing, and using a telephone. The photographs are large enough to be easily handled but may be of limited use for the blind and partially sighted.

The leaflet identifies the skills that can be developed. These include: comprehension and verbal expression; linguistic structures; improving communication; and cognitive skills. It also outlines a set of simple instructions and describes a variety of ways that facilitators, teachers, or carers might use the cards to develop the use of different verb tenses, prepositions, adjectives, and language extension. There are examples of how the pack can be used creatively to explore issues such as personal history and emotions.

The eight models shown in the photographs range from children to older people. While two of the models are from different ethnic backgrounds, there are no learning disabled models. Some of the activities demonstrated reflect rather stereotypical roles in terms of both age and gender, but this may be helpful for working with older people.

This is a flexible aid and can be used with individuals and small groups, without the need for additional materials. It lends itself to informal settings and the exercises described can be used independently or as part of a more structured course.

This is one of the ColorCards sequencing series that develops in complexity from this 3-step 'Basic Sequences' pack through the 4-step sequencing entitled 'Daily Living', to the 6-step sequencing, 'Social Situations', and the 8-step sequencing, 'Activities and Events'. These other titles are still available from the distributor and were reviewed in the original database publication but are not included here as they pre-date 1993.

ColorCards: everyday objects

FORMAT: Boxed card set, A5 cards (x48); notes
AUDIENCE: Children and adults with learning disabilities
PRICE: £23.75 + VAT + 12% p&p
PRODUCER: Bicester: Winslow Press, 1988, revised 1994 (to be revised March 1999)
DISTRIBUTOR: Winslow Press
ISBN: 0 86388 03 8 X

This resource is one of the ColorCards photograph series that was reviewed in the original publication. There are nine other titles in this series.

Everyday objects consists of a set of 48 laminated photo cards showing everyday objects, including items of food, toys, household objects, personal objects such as keys, a comb, spectacles, and children's clothing. A leaflet accompanying the cards suggests some ways of using them. These include language comprehension, naming and describing objects, talking about associated words or objects, grouping the cards into different categories, and memory games.

Some of the cards might be used to trigger discussion. For example, the picture of a television might start a discussion about programmes an individual likes to watch. Food cards might be helpful in planning shopping lists, and household objects cards could help someone think about what they will need when moving into their own home. Facilitators could supplement these cards with more of their own – for example, using magazine pictures stuck on to card or in some instances using actual objects depending on the aims of their session and the needs of the group or individual. The cards are versatile and can be used with people of varying abilities in different ways.

Colour communication picture stickers

FORMAT: Stickers: Pack A – A4 instruction sheet, colour picture stickers (420) and word labels; Pack B – A4 instruction sheet, colour picture stickers (180), and word labels; Pack C – A4 instruction sheet, colour picture stickers (240) and word labels. Also now available on CD-Rom or disk (IBM compatible)
AUDIENCE: People with moderate to several learning disabilities
PRICE: £52.00 + VAT (Pack A); £29.75 + VAT (Pack B); £36.00 + VAT (Pack C); £145.00 + VAT for complete set plus the Health Care Pack; £255.00 + VAT (CD-Rom); £195.00 + VAT (Disk); all plus 12% p&p
PRODUCER: USA: Imaginart Communication Products, 1985, reprinted 1993
DISTRIBUTOR: Winslow Press

Each pack contains instruction sheets, sheets of stickers representing a range of objects, actions, and emotions, and word labels to match the pictures. The packs are designed to help children and adults with communication difficulties achieve independence. They can be used with people who have moderate to severe learning disabilities and/or physical disabilities to increase communication and to develop language. The stickers can be used to create individual 'augmentative communication' devices – for example, they can be placed on boards, in notebooks, and on overlays for electronic communication devices. The images can be changed as the user progresses or as needs change.

There are word labels in each pack to accompany the picture stickers. These labels could be used with people who have some reading skills, but are less useful for those people with learning disabilities who cannot read.

Pack A contains 420 images and word labels covering family and friends, the home environment, feelings, clothing, common activities, common events, food, shops, and services. Most of the images of people are white; those in the emotions section include both male and female images.

Pack B contains 180 images representing more complex ideas such as spatial concepts – for example, over, under, or between. They also depict body parts, animals, and occupations.

Pack C contains 240 images representing common activities, travelling by bus, food, money, television, places, people, animals, school, and work.

A pack dedicated to health care is also available, although this was not reviewed. The distributor describes the pack as a collection for anyone involved in providing health care. This would include primary healthcare teams, care workers and hospital staff. The 180 stickers with matching words cover activities, basic needs, feelings, health, people, words, and phrases.

The resource is based on an American design, so some symbols may be unfamiliar while other, familiar, symbols may be missing. Also included are a few blank squares to create new symbols that may more appropriately reflect the individual's experience and needs. The A5 ring-bound organiser is portable and can be divided into different sections such as food, family, emotions, transport, and health. These can be filled with symbols appropriate to the individual. The stickers can be used on portable boards, in a special notebook that can be divided into sections, or in pocket picture holders that can take up to 64 stickers in clear vinyl pockets.

These stickers are now available on CD-Rom or disk, organised under specific subjects. This format gives the user the flexibility to make the images smaller or larger, to change colours or customise the images, and to create labels.

Colour me loud

FORMAT: Video, 25 mins
AUDIENCE: Adults with moderate learning disabilities
PRICE: £35.00 + VAT for statutory organisations; £20.00 + VAT for unfunded groups
PRODUCER: London: Mental Health Media, 1994
DISTRIBUTOR: Mental Health Media

This video, originally broadcast in Channel 4's *People first* series, focuses on the work of three different self-advocacy groups run by adults with learning disabilities in Nottingham, Newcastle, and Avon. People with learning disabilities speak movingly about their own involvement in the groups and about the value of self-advocacy to their lives. They speak, throughout, in their own words. There is no subtitling or sign-language interpretation. All of the people featured are white.

The video focuses on three individuals who describe the changes that joining a group has made to their lives. The title comes from the strong and colourful pictures drawn by one of them, Kevin, who uses them to explore the painful memories of 20 years in hospital. In hospital, he says, his world used to be grey and black and he kept all his colours inside. Now he is able to let his true colours out. The video includes a section showing Kevin and members of Advocacy in Action running a training course for social services staff about the experiences of service users.

Although the experiences of each individual are very different, common themes begin to emerge – for example, the importance of building self-confidence, and of the mutual support provided by the group. Other themes include the importance of maintaining user-control and the group's independence and wider issues of discrimination and institutionalisation. In addition, it gives a brief background history of the development of self-advocacy in the UK. *Colour me loud* could be used as an introduction to self-advocacy for small groups of adults with moderate learning disabilities, especially if they are thinking of setting up or joining a self-advocacy group. It could also be used with carers and other professionals to trigger discussion about learning disability and to explore the value of self-advocacy.

Contact a family

FORMAT: Pack – booklets (x8)
AUDIENCE: Parents, carers, families
PRICE: £11.00 inc.
PRODUCER: London: Contact a Family, 1996
DISTRIBUTOR: Contact a Family

This group action pack contains eight booklets offering guidance and support for families who care for children with disabilities and special needs – i.e. any kind of disability or medical condition. The pack offers practical guidelines and information for anyone wishing to start a mutual support group. It also includes a useful guide for professionals who work with a support group.

The A4 booklets are available singly, or as part of a complete pack and there are suitable publications for both local and national groups. The subject areas covered are: Starting a local parents' group; Holding an open meeting; Attracting and keeping members; Local campaigning; Professional workers and parent support groups; Starting a national support group; Developing a national support group; Fundraising for parents' groups; and Producing a newsletter for your group. New titles will be added to the pack as they are developed.

Each booklet follows a similar format. It breaks each subject area down into clearly defined steps – for example, Starting a local parents' group considers the practical implications of starting a group as well as the need to think through processes such as deciding group aims and creating a group identity.

Several different authors wrote the booklets. In some there are examples of other people's experiences, including those representing the needs of families from black and minority ethnic groups.

The pack was developed on the basis of what parents have asked for and shared over some years, and lists of useful resources and contacts are included.

Contact a Family is a national charitable organisation that provides a network of support for around 1000 local groups in the UK and incorporates over 300 national groups for specific and rare conditions. They welcome calls for further help and advice.

Coping with death

FORMAT: Video, 15 mins
AUDIENCE: People with learning disabilities
PRICE: £25.00 inc. (advocacy groups); £28.00 inc. (other groups)
PRODUCER: Rotherham: Speakup Self Advocacy, 1995
DISTRIBUTOR: Speakup Self Advocacy

This video was made by learning disabled people to help others with learning disabilities cope with loss through bereavement. Members of the Speakup Self Advocacy Group explore the issue of death. The narrator, who has a learning disability, suggests that death is difficult to think or talk about. He describes what happens when someone we know dies, how final this is, and that it might mean very different things to people who hold different beliefs.

There is footage and descriptions of Christian funeral procedures, including cremation and burial. Members of the group relate their experiences of losing someone they were close to. Viewers are told that talking helps – 'It's O.K. to cry and talk' and, although there are difficult feelings involved, people can help each other. Organisations where people can go to talk about their feelings are mentioned, including Cruse and the Samaritans, but it might be advisable to locate these or similar organisations in your area.

Each individual talks about how they have chosen to remember someone who has died – for example, taking flowers to a grave. Viewers are also reminded that when we die, which we must inevitably do, other people will remember us with love in their hearts.

This is a deceptively simple yet powerful film. It might be useful as an introduction to the subject or to show someone who has been bereaved recently what happens next. The video is best suited to viewing in an informal setting, whether by an individual or a group. While no special training is required to facilitate the watching of this film, it might be advisable for someone with counselling skills to be present. The clear dialogue and large print in the film may make it accessible to people with sight difficulties.

This video was commissioned by Rotherham Social Services as part of the Rotherham Communication Strategy. It was supported by National Lottery funding through the Arts Council of England. Bubble Media co-produced the film and any group wishing to produce their own video are invited to contact them.

Cracking crime – a learning and resource pack on coping with crime for people with learning difficulties

FORMAT: Pack – video, 30 mins; ringbinder, 71-pages, illustrated; book, 48-pages, illustrated
AUDIENCE: People with learning disabilities
PRICE: £76.37 inc. + p&p; £23.50 + p&p (special schools/self-advocacy group price)
PRODUCER: Bristol Norah Fry Research Centre, 1995
DISTRIBUTOR: Pavilion Publishing Ltd
ISBN: 1 871080 74 6

A video pack in which a group of people with learning disabilities look at what constitutes a crime and how to obtain justice, with materials designed to stimulate group discussion. The materials aim to encourage people to practise specific skills through role-play.

Cracking crime was produced as part of a two-year research project carried out by the Norah Fry Research Centre. It was conceived and produced by victims of crime who have learning disabilities. The resource consists of a ringbinder, a video, and a book and is intended for use by people with learning disabilities, individually with support, or in groups. The materials can be used together or separately, according to the needs of the learner. The resource was tested by students from a further education class who contributed more ideas – for example, on sexual harassment.

The video is in three sections. What is a crime? looks first at the major crimes against people with learning disabilities reported in the media – such as murder, sexual abuse, and kidnapping – and then goes on to give examples of everyday crimes like harassment, physical attacks, or racial abuse. In the second section, Getting justice, the presenters ask if any of these things have happened to you and explore what you can do about it. The video suggests that you first tell someone you know (for example by drawing) and then go to the police. There is an interview with a police officer about how to report a crime, the interview procedure, the role of solicitors, and legal aid. The video briefly explains the role of the Crown Prosecution Service and then explores going to court. It uses the example of a case of physical harassment of a black worker with learning disabilities by his employer, a case which happened in real life but never went to court. Inside the courtroom, the different roles are explained: the public gallery; jury; judge; and defendant. The prosecuting barrister, played by a person with a learning disability, cross-examines the witness. The video does not explore in any depth the emotional impact of being cross-examined. The final section, Getting together, looks at setting up support groups. The group interview a worker from Victim Support, and talk to Julie Boniface who set up VOICE, an organisation which supports families of victims of sexual abuse. Others in the group talk about doing a play or writing a poem, as a way of expressing their feelings about harassment.

The pack gives the background to the project and suggests ways of using the video. It includes extracts from the video script – for example, from some of the interviews – and follows them with a sheet of questions and answers and things to do. In the section about the police, for example, the pack suggests asking 'Has anyone ever told the police about something? What happened?' It suggests a group using the resource might visit their local police station and talk about crime. The questions, answers, and suggestions for activities are written in clear language and the sheets could be photocopied for use by a group.

The book, *Coping with crime*, can be used on its own if video is not an appropriate medium, or in conjunction with the video. It aims to enable people to understand what a crime is, how to prevent crimes and abuse, and what to do if you are a victim. It provides ideas for group discussion and role play to develop skills to prevent and cope with victimisation specific to people with learning disabilities. Each section begins with questions and answers to introduce the particular issue. These are followed by situations to act out and discuss, and other suggested activities. For example, the section on Remembering begins by asking 'What things do you need to remember if a crime happens to you?' It suggests: what people look like; when it happened; where it happened; and who else saw it. The section goes on to suggest activities such as, in a group, without warning, ask one person to leave the room. Ask the others to describe what that person was wearing and other features – height, age, hair colour, and so on. Progressively more complex activities to develop remembering skills are introduced and the section ends with an activity to learn how to draw a plan.

The resource can be used flexibly, according to the needs of a group or individual, either in response to actual crime, in connection with crime reported in the media, together with other learning packs (for example, on sexuality or assertiveness), or as part of a structured learning programme about crime. It aims to provide materials for a structured course of 3–12 sessions. *Cracking crime* provides a good example of what people can achieve, and could also be used in self-advocacy groups to initiate a similar project.

Dealing with bereavement – a curriculum pack for youth workers

FORMAT: Multimedia – A5, illustrated introduction and briefing, 93 pages; groupwork exercises, 40 pages; activity cards (x74); A5 newsheet folding to A3.
AUDIENCE: 11- to 19-year-olds, people with learning disabilities, youth workers
AUTHOR: Green, J.
PRICE: £14.99 inc.
PRODUCER: Youth Work Press, 1995
DISTRIBUTOR: Leicester Youth Work Press

This pack is for youth workers and others who work with young people to enable young people to explore and express their feelings in relation to bereavement and loss. It is aimed at 11- to 19-year-olds (Key Stages 3 and 4) and young people with learning disabilities.

The pack consists of booklets, activity cards, and a newsheet contained in a laminated card box.

In the introduction and briefing notes there is an introduction and sections on the psychology of bereavement, the culture of bereavement, practical guidelines on groupwork, and appendices.

The groupwork exercises contain 10 activities on topics such as religious beliefs, bereavement and physical pain, loss, and peer support. The exercises provide details of aims, method, resources required, timing, and facilitator's notes. Some of the exercises require copies of other information resources. The focus of the pack is on anticipated rather than sudden losses and it does not deal with the effects on young people of group tragedies, suicide, murder, or dramatic death.

A participatory approach is used to exploring issues of loss and bereavement, including matching card games and role play. It requires skilled facilitation and an ability to support young people on issues of loss and bereavement, working at their own pace. It also requires knowledge of, and sensitivity to, the range of cultural responses to loss and bereavement. The pack can be used to devise one-off sessions exploring particular facets of bereavement, but is probably best used in a series of sessions with adequate time between them to allow young people to work on the issues at their own pace. It can be used in youth and community settings or possibly in classroom settings.

The pack encourages exploration of loss and bereavement in a multicultural and multi-faith context and includes information on, for example, funeral arrangements and mourning observances in Buddhism, Christianity, Hinduism, Islam, Judaism, and Sikhism. The exercises also explore the impact of religious prejudice and intolerance, and the notes raise the issue of loss in a same-sex relationship. Notes and a drawing exercise are included for use with young people with learning disabilities.

Don't call us names

FORMAT: Video, 14 mins
AUDIENCE: Young people and adults with learning disabilities
PRICE: £20 inc. (£15.00 inc. for Enable branches and self-advocacy groups)
PRODUCER: Glasgow: Enable/Glasgow Film and Video Workshop, 1994
DISTRIBUTOR: Enable

This video, produced by Enable (formerly the Scottish Society for the Mentally Handicapped), aims to build up the confidence of young people with learning disabilities to speak out when faced with insulting and abusive behaviour. In 1993, research by Enable showed that many people with learning disabilities experienced the problem of being called names. This video shows the hurt, anger, and humiliation felt by people when this happens. Included in the video is a young black man, a police officer, and a young white woman who do not have learning disabilities but who have also experienced similar problems with name calling.

The video uses some drama, but it mainly deals with individuals speaking about their experiences and what they do when they are called names. This includes telling somebody about it, ignoring it, or assertively confronting the individuals involved. The video stresses the importance of not keeping these experiences to yourself.

The police officer and others explain that it is often ignorance, showing off, and sometimes fear, that causes people – particularly teenagers – to name-call. Advice is given about how to deal with a variety of situations both in the street and in work situations. The video concludes with information about Enable; additional information about organisations outside Scotland would need to be provided if relevant.

This video is appropriate for groups of adults and young people with learning disabilities in a variety of informal and educational settings. It could be used as part of assertiveness skills courses or self-advocacy. There is no supplementary material.

Don't smoke – you make me choke

FORMAT: Video, 12 mins; notes, 4-pages
AUDIENCE: 8- to 12-year-olds (Key Stages 2 and 3), older pupils with special needs
PRICE: £8.50 inc.
PRODUCER: Bradford: Resources for Learning, 1995
DISTRIBUTOR: Resources for Learning
This resource was developed in association with teachers and children in a special school in Bradford. It includes a video and two sides of notes for teachers. It is aimed at 8- to 12-year-old pupils (Key Stages 2 and 3) and the notes suggest that it would be useful for older pupils with special needs.
Throughout the video, a young presenter asks questions that are answered by street interviews and stylised comic strips – situations presented in sequences of still drawn images with voice-overs. The situations include a couple dancing and young people buying cigarettes from a shop. The video can be watched all the way through or paused at specific points for discussion. Clear graphics tell the facilitator when to pause the video and the presenter asks questions to guide the discussion. These questions are also included in the teachers' notes, with further information about smoking.
The resource explores why people start smoking, smoking and the law, the effects on health and safety, addiction, and the social and financial costs of smoking. The main theme and message of the video is choice – you can choose whether or not to start smoking and choose whether or not to give up.
Although structured for discussion, the video is didactic in style – both asking questions and giving answers. More complex discussion on some of the issues – for example, addiction or why people start to smoke – would need a lot of input from teachers. The choice of a young person as presenter may be attractive to young people, but those interviewed on the street, with one exception, are not of school age, nearly all white, and nearly all are men. The producers state that the resource would be useful for 'older pupils with special needs'. However, it consists primarily of talking heads and verbal information, and neither video nor notes indicate ways of working without relying on writing or discussion skills. The choice of a young person as presenter could be a useful stimulus to begin creative work with young people on what they might include in a video about smoking for their peers.

Drug pics

FORMAT: Pack – A3 write-on wipe-off boards (x14); lesson plan, 17 pages with A4 worksheets (x14); pens (x4); board eraser
AUDIENCE: 11- to 16-year-olds (Key Stage 3); young people with learning disabilities
PRICE: £78.50 inc.
PRODUCER: Manchester: Headon Productions, 1996
DISTRIBUTOR: Headon Productions
This pack is intended for use with young people aged 11 to 16 years (Key Stage 3), including young people with learning disabilities. It is designed to support drug education programmes in schools but could also be used in colleges and youth and community settings. The pack aims to inform about what drugs and substances look like, the effects on the body, and other related issues such as the risks involved, the law, and medical uses.

The pack contains laminated wipe boards, a lesson plan, pens, and a board eraser in a PVC case. The lesson plan includes materials for a drugs awareness session. The plan details the aim of the lesson, resources required, methods, and notes. Some activities require additional drugs awareness leaflets, pamphlets, and books (available from TACADE or Lifeline). The methods are interactive and users will require basic group facilitation skills. The publishers state that the pack has been evaluated in local education authorities.

Early listening skills

FORMAT: Pack, 288-pages, illustrated
AUDIENCE: Professionals working with pre-school children with delayed listening skills, and those who are deaf or hard of hearing
PRICE: £35.45 + p&p
PRODUCER: Bicester: Winslow Press, 1995
DISTRIBUTOR: Winslow Press
Early listening skills is intended for use by professionals working with pre-school children who have underdeveloped listening skills, associated with language delay, hearing loss, or other communication difficulties. It contains ideas and exercises to stimulate and develop auditory attention and perceptual skills in children who have delayed listening skills associated with hearing loss or communication difficulties. The pack is structured to follow the developmental sequence in which a child's auditory skills progress. The early sections aim to develop basic listening and hearing skills needed by a child before she or he can attach meaning to sound. These include: discovering sound; exploring sound makers; detecting sound and silence; discrimination and sound recognition; and finding sound. The later sections cover more complex auditory skills such as rhythm and sequencing and remembering sounds. A section on listening to speech looks at the way adults can talk to children to encourage their use of language. It deals with information-giving words and phrases and the role of the speaker's gestures in aiding or hindering language use. The last sections of the pack describe holiday listening projects and topics for the school curriculum. At the end there is a comprehensive list of sounds and soundmakers that can be used.
Each section has the same structure. It begins with an introduction to help the user decide whether the child is ready for this particular stage. This is followed by one main teaching activity which aims to use a range of sound makers to develop the listening skills in that section. These activities are clearly set out in a step-by-step sequence, including: lists of the materials needed; useful words and phrases for the facilitator to use; and ways of developing the activity. The pack also suggests further activities for school or nursery and home. These are intended to help children generalise and reinforce the skills learned. The home activities aim to use the child's everyday routines to learn about sound and listening. Each section also includes a list of sounds to use (ranging from telephones to drills to the human voice) and a checklist to help monitor the child's progress.
This comprehensive pack is geared towards helping facilitators structure and select activities for an individual child's needs and develop an appropriate programme of work. Many of the sections and activities will be useful for children with severe hearing loss or impairment. It would also be useful for the development of concentration, focus, and attention in young children with and without disabilities.

Epilepsy and you

FORMAT: Video, 15 mins; guide, 15-pages, illustrated
AUDIENCE: People with learning disabilities and epilepsy, carers, support workers
PRICE: £41.12 inc.
PRODUCER: Brighton: Pavilion Publishing Ltd, 1996
DISTRIBUTOR: Pavilion Publishing

This video-assisted training pack aims to help people with learning disabilities understand and manage their epilepsy. It was made with the involvement of people with epilepsy. The video uses interviews in which people describe their own experiences, together with explanations by specialists. It covers what epilepsy is, different kinds of seizure, how epilepsy is treated, what to do when someone has a seizure, and ways of managing your epilepsy.

The video describes research into epilepsy that suggests some people can learn the signs that immediately precede a seizure, and can reduce the likelihood that they have a seizure. It suggests techniques to help people become aware when a seizure is about to happen: saying their name repeatedly or moving their arms and legs. It gives clear guidelines to other people about what to do when a seizure happens. The final section of the video looks at methods of managing seizures – for example, showing someone working with a support worker to keep a seizure diary.

The accompanying facilitators' notes, written by a psychologist, suggest how the video could be used with groups or individuals. The notes suggest small group work is more effective because participants learn from each other and can begin to address issues of stigma. Three sessions are outlined, each lasting about an hour, with some work between each session for individuals to do with a support worker. The training looks at three main issues: medication; safety; and using a diary. It is suggested that the video is shown twice, in session 1 and again in session 2, when viewers are asked to look particularly at issues around medication and safety.

The session plans give clear instructions to facilitators. They are activity based and the notes include photocopiable worksheets to help people explain what happens when they have a seizure. Two of the worksheets involve quite complex written questions and people with reading difficulties would need help from a support worker to answer them. One worksheet uses three line drawings to explain what a seizure is. The notes also contain a handout classifying seizures. This uses complex medical terms and would need to be adapted for work with people with learning disabilities. There is a list of other relevant publications at the end of the notes.

This is a useful resource, especially for carers, though it may need further adaptation for use with people with learning disabilities. The sound on the video is occasionally poor, and the video sections are not clearly signposted. However, the interviews with people with epilepsy make it a valuable tool to look at people's fears – whether to address worries about the seizures themselves or fears about the reactions of others to their seizures.

Everything you ever wanted to know about safer sex but nobody ever bothered to tell you

FORMAT: Cassette, 30 mins; booklet, 20-pages
AUDIENCE: Adults with learning disabilities

PRICE: £11.00 + p&p
PRODUCER: London: People First, 1994
DISTRIBUTOR: People First
This is a resource by and for adults with learning disabilities. The cassette is intended for people without reading skills and tells when to turn the page in the booklet to view the corresponding pictures. However, people may need some help establishing which page they are on to begin with.
The booklet encourages people with learning disabilities to recognise their rights to sex education, privacy, adult status, and choice, including choice about sexual orientation. Some local information is given on where to go for further information and advice on sexual matters. There is a brief explanation of HIV and AIDS using cartoon figures, including some dos and don'ts for safer sex and advice about using condoms. Some of the pictures (particularly those describing HIV) may be confusing and it would be helpful for a facilitator to be available to clarify the information using supplementary materials if necessary. The spoken words on the tape are roughly the same as those in the written text but, whereas in the book information is set out in separate paragraphs and 'bullet' points for easy digestion, some of the information on the tape is read very quickly without pauses between points. A facilitator may need to make use of the pause button and check understanding. There is also some occasional background noise on the tape. The booklet could be used as a starting point for discussion or as a reminder of some of the main points for those who have recently attended a sex education course. The resource provides a summary of some key points about safer sex in the context of rights and self-advocacy. However, it represents only a small part of the sex education that most people will need. Addresses and phone numbers for health and family planning clinics in the Camden area of North London are given; information about services in other areas will need to be added by the facilitator. There is also information about consultation, information, and training services offered in London by People First.

Extending horizons

FORMAT: Pack, unpaged, illustrated
AUDIENCE: People with severe learning disabilities, teachers, parents, staff in day centres
PRICE: Free + £5.00 p&p
PRODUCER: Coventry: NCET, 1995
DISTRIBUTOR: Special Educational Needs and Inclusion, BECTA
ISBN: 1853793256
Extending Horizons is a comprehensive resource about using computers and other technologies in work with people with severe and profound learning disabilities in mainstream schools, special schools, and colleges. It is the product of a project that enables teachers, lecturers, advisers, and parents to share their experiences of using new technologies to enhance learning in people with learning disabilities.
The pack gives an overview of a range of issues and applications for technology. It consists of an A4 ring binder containing articles, resource lists, and suppliers. The articles are accounts of practical experience; in each case the focus is on the principle of the activity and its learning objectives rather than on specific software or hardware solutions. The pack covers such topics as multisensory rooms, e-mail, soundbeam, leisure software, using symbols, CD-i, control technology, touch screens, floor robots, and data logging.
An Issues section explores the theoretical and technical background to projects, and includes articles about communication, identity, imagination, effective use of technology, geography software, the use

of IT in assessment and planning, and IT policies. A glossary explains the technical terms mentioned and there are lists of resources and suppliers.
This would be a useful resource to anyone working with people with learning disabilities in schools. It is also relevant to staff working with adults in day services. The pack provides a wealth of tested and practical ideas, grounded in educational theory. The project has built up a support network of organisations and individuals, and addresses are included in a Contacts section. Parents, teachers, governors, and advisers are invited to contribute their own experiences of using technology with people with learning disabilities. Further publications and updates arising from the project are expected. These can be added to the existing ring binder.
NCET changed its name to British Educational Communications and Technology Agency (BECTA) in 1998.

Feeling blue

FORMAT: Book, 66-pages, illustrated
AUDIENCE: Adults with learning disabilities
AUTHOR: Hollins, S., Curran, J. and Webb, B. (illustrator)
PRICE: £10.00 inc.
PRODUCER: London: St George's Hospital Medical School, 1995
DISTRIBUTOR: Royal College of Psychiatrists, Book Sales
ISBN: 1 874439 09 5
This colour picture book was written by two psychiatrists and is part of the *Books beyond words* series for people with learning disabilities. The 33 illustrations tell a story in clear and expressive pictures. Readers are encouraged to tell the story in their own words. There is a blank page between each of the pictures where people can draw their own pictures or add their own words if they wish. Words for each page are included at the end of the book for those who prefer a ready-made story.
The story follows Ron, a young man who feels sad. His friends try to interest him in going swimming or watching TV, but Ron refuses to join them. One of them tries to persuade Ron, and Ron gets angry with him. The friend phones a doctor who gradually enables Ron to talk about how he is feeling. They look at photos of Ron when he was happy. Eventually Ron feels better and begins to join in with his friends again. The story also includes two additional pictures to describe prescribing and taking medication, explaining that 'sometimes talking is not enough'. The first of these shows the doctor explaining the prescription to Ron; the second shows a close-up of the tablets with Ron's hand about to take one.
The book could be used by someone with limited reading skills or it could be read and talked through with another person. The pictures are very powerful and facial expressions vividly convey feelings – there are no distracting details, just strong colour and expressive body language. It could be used with groups or individual adults to explore feelings of unhappiness or depression. The characters vary in age and ethnic background.

Feeling poorly: a complete assessment and training pack to help people with learning disabilities communicate effectively about symptoms of illness and pain

FORMAT: Pack – ringbinder, 85-pages; resource sheets; communication aid cards (available separately); bingo cards
AUDIENCE: People with learning disabilities, primary healthcare teams

PRICE: £145.00 + p&p (full pack); £39.95 + p&p (communication aid cards only)
PRODUCER: Brighton: Pavilion Publishing, 1998
DISTRIBUTOR: Pavilion Publishing Ltd.

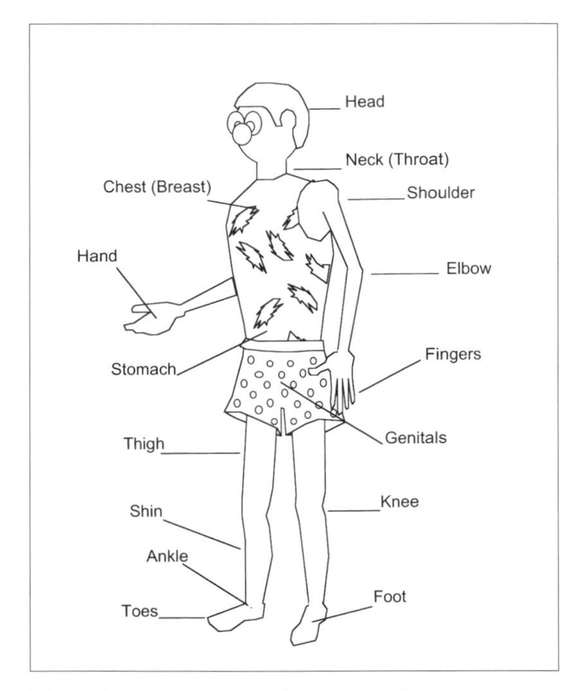

The aim of this training pack is to improve access to mainstream health care and screening programmes for people with learning disabilities by improving their knowledge of illness and their ability to communicate effectively with GPs and other health professionals.
The pack comprises a comprehensive 20-session training programme divided into three sections. Section one provides information about the body and how it works – senses, organs, eating, and breathing. The second section includes aids to good communication covering thinking and feeling, how to understand pain and illness, and how to express them to others. The last section concentrates on how to use GP services effectively, meeting a real GP, learning about surgeries, routine equipment, and what is expected of patients. The pack does not include any references to sexual health.

It contains a wide variety of communication aids, including very expressive drawings to accompany the sessions and fun activities such as blind tasting of food, fingerprinting, role plays, and quizzes.
'*Feeling poorly*' is designed to be flexible and facilitators could use it with groups in a variety of settings. For example, it would help community nurses and support staff to teach people about their bodies and how to express their needs to health professionals more effectively. It could help self-advocacy groups become more involved in healthcare services and support schemes for people living independently, and it also includes material to enable GPs to have a better understanding of their patients. It is most suitable for people with moderate to severe difficulties and would be good for people with sight difficulties. The drawings are clear enough for some partial sight, but the adaptability and variety of teaching methods makes it accessible for those with little or no vision. The majority of illustrations are of white people.
This training pack was developed by Dr. Karen Dodd of Surrey Oaklands NHS Trust. It was piloted with help from East Surrey Health Authority and Mid Surrey Community Team, with involvement from both service users and staff.

First Steps to Parenthood

FORMAT: Pack, 100-pages
AUDIENCE: Parents with learning disabilities, primary healthcare teams
PRICE: £65.00 + p&p
PRODUCER: Brighton: Pavilion Publishing, 1997
DISTRIBUTOR: Pavilion Publishing Ltd.
This pack was designed for working with parents, or prospective parents, one or both of whom have a learning disability. It could be used by a wide range of

professionals, including midwives, health visitors, community nurses, social workers, and support workers.

The aims of this resource are to assist in the assessment of a person's understanding of child development and to avoid some of the problems that may face learning disabled people when they become parents. It seeks to identify individual needs, such as practical training, information, and support. The manual does not set out to address or meet those needs.

The pack includes an introduction and instructions on how to use the manual, which consists of seven sections, covering pregnancy and birth through to adolescence. Each unit consists of photocopiable sheets, which contain structured questions, designed to act as a springboard for discussion and to lead to further questions. These are accompanied by black-and-white drawings that illustrate the text. These might need enlarging for use with partially sighted people.

The parents, children, and other people illustrated are all white and there is no information about how cultural differences might affect attitudes and views about pregnancy and parenthood.

This pack can be used with an individual parent or in a group. It is suitable for a variety of formal or informal settings. Units can be used individually or as part of a more comprehensive assessment. Ongoing training is likely to continue into adolescence.

The authors are a clinical psychologist and a senior registrar in child psychiatry. The basic questions were used to teach and assess people in parent-craft sessions provided by Exeter Parenting Service. The pack is currently used to assist assessment.

Food and Drink. Sequencing overlays: set 2

FORMAT: Transparent cards (x24); notes, 10-pages
AUDIENCE: Children and adults with learning disabilities
PRICE: £13.95 + VAT
PRODUCER: Leicester: Taskmaster Limited, 1993
DISTRIBUTOR: Taskmaster Ltd.
CODE: T928

These are sequencing cards on nutrition for children with impoverished or disordered language development and for those with specific sequencing or coding disabilities. A set of 24 colour images are printed on transparent plastic cards that can be overlaid to produce composite pictures made up of three or four layers. This boxed set comes with notes giving a few suggestions for ways in which the cards can be used. The set contains four 3-card and three 4-card sequences. The 3-card sequences are: cornet, ice cream, and chocolate wafer; bread, butter, and jam; toast, butter, and baked beans; and pizza base, tomato puree, and cheese topping. The 4-card sequences are: paper case, cake filling, icing on cake, and cherry top; sponge cake, icing on cake, candles, and candle flames; table, table cloth, place settings, and food.

The notes suggest that 'educationalists will find them particularly useful for children with impoverished or disordered language development and those with specific sequencing or coding disabilities (for example, autistic continuum, perceptual disorders, dyspraxia).' The images are not age-specific and could be used with older children or adults.

By placing the cards in the correct order, the person using them has the opportunity to practice hand and eye co-ordination and to develop a sense of a logical sequence of events. Because the cards are transparent, another goal is to assemble the cards so that left and right are aligned correctly, thus introducing the concept of left and right. Alternatively, the cards could be laid out on a surface from left to right, preparing the way for using more conventional picture sequences. The cards could be used to develop language in a variety of ways: nouns (for example, toast, butter, jam); verbs (for example, 'you toast the bread and then you spread the butter'); spatial concepts (for example, 'you put the butter on first then put the jam on top'); and concepts of cause and effect (for example, 'what would happen if you put the jam on before the butter?'). The sequences could also be used to prepare people for a practical food preparation session or as a follow-up to this.

Made in a strong plastic, colourful and smooth to touch, these cards are enjoyable to use as well as versatile. Others in the same series are: *Daily routine*, *Play and school*, and *The living world*.

Four stories

FORMAT: Video pack – video, 30 mins; booklet, 16-pages

AUDIENCE: People with mild to moderate learning disabilities

PRICE: £48.00 + VAT

PRODUCER: New Zealand: Family Planning Association, 1997

DISTRIBUTOR: Pavilion Publishing Ltd

ISBN: 0958330468

This video pack from New Zealand was made for people with mild to moderate learning disabilities. It is designed to help people think and talk about relationships and sexuality, and can help parents and others who provide them with support. It might be less useful for someone with sight difficulties who would find the format and dialogue confusing.

'Things are changing ...', the accompanying booklet tells us. Learning disabled people are supported to live more independently in the community and, for younger people in particular, this will include wanting to build the kind of relationships that are part of normal life.

This pack does not set out to provide easy answers, nor is it offering sex education or sexual health information. It is about relationships and the worries and problems that can arise, as well as the joys.

There are four scenarios, dramatised by learning disabled people and others. Each story has a theme: The decision to get married; Setting boundaries; Same sex attraction; and Support for parenting.

The booklet was written for use with the video. There are summaries of each story and questions to help the viewer(s) think and talk about the issues involved. The stories all have happy endings – for example, Raumati gets to keep her baby because she is fortunate to have family support, which might not be the case for some women.

It is advisable to watch the video first otherwise some of the questions in the booklet will not make sense. It can be viewed by people in their own home or used for group work. The booklet suggests ways of using it as a structured course.

This resource was made for a New Zealand audience and reflects the language and ethnic mix of that culture. Two of the stories are about Maori people who have learning disabilities and their families. The information in the leaflet about organisations and resources is, therefore, not applicable. Potential users should contact their local Family Planning Association for more information.

This pack was produced by the New Zealand Family Planning Association, a project advisory group, and includes contributions from health authorities and other organisations.

Getting better: a video training pack to help people with learning difficulties get the best out of their GP

FORMAT: Video, 15 mins; booklet, 27-pages, illustrated
AUDIENCE: People with learning disabilities, primary healthcare teams
AUTHOR: Band, R.
PRICE: £125.00 + p&p
PRODUCER: Brighton: Pavilion Publishing, 1997
DISTRIBUTOR: Pavilion Publishing Ltd
ISBN: 1900600560

This video training pack aims to assist people with learning disabilities to get help from their GP. It consists of a video, a workbook for carers and support workers, and supplementary work cards for use as handouts. The pack was commissioned by the Elfrida Society Access to Health project. They involved people with learning disabilities by asking them to design materials and present their thoughts about getting the best out of their GP.

The video portrays the story of a young, black woman with learning disabilities who becomes ill and needs help to get better. The issues covered include being ill and what to do about it, making an appointment, preparing for the visit, registering with a GP, making a complaint, how to change doctors, and prescriptions and medicines. The characters are people with learning disabilities, mainly young, of both genders, and from different black and minority ethnic groups.

The booklet is intended for support workers to use with groups of learning disabled people. It contains comprehensive preparatory activities and helpful checklists for facilitators. Each of the sections on the video comes with helpful and wide ranging discussion points and imaginative activities such as role plays, invitations to visit by a receptionist, or researching information provided by surgeries. It is a visual resource with limited use for people with sight difficulties.

The resource can be used in more wide ranging ways – for example, as part of a course on health awareness, recognising and understanding ill health, and in promoting self-advocacy. Primary healthcare teams would find this an invaluable aid to their own learning about how to respond to disabled patients, and it could be used successfully by any healthcare pressure group anxious to improve the interface between patients with learning disabilities and health care teams. It would be useful preparatory material for groups wanting to be more involved in the work of Primary Care Groups.

Getting in touch: ways of working with people with severe learning disabilities and extensive support needs

FORMAT: Book, 34-pages
AUDIENCE: People with profound and multiple disabilities, support staff
AUTHOR: Caldwell, P.
PRICE: £11.95 + p&p
PRODUCER: Brighton: Pavilion Publishing, 1996
DISTRIBUTOR: Pavilion Publishing Ltd.
ISBN: 1 900600 05 6

The author of this book, Phoebe Caldwell, began working with people with profound and multiple disabilities, including those with severe sensory deficits and challenging behaviours, as an occupational therapy helper. She has since developed distinctive ways of working and of developing equipment through which to communicate.

This book is a report of a training programme in which she worked with 60 support staff and individuals with learning disabilities. The report aims to be a practical guide for staff in residential homes and day services, occupational therapists, physiotherapists, community nurses, and others working with people with profound and multiple disabilities or 'challenging behaviour'.

Caldwell's approach involves finding an appropriate language through which to engage with people in meaningful interactions. This language need not be based on words but may involve vibrations, movement, sounds, and touch. Its premise is that some people who do not have language have learned to 'talk' to themselves. Using people's own language it is possible to get in touch and gain their attention. The book aims to introduce these ideas using the examples that occurred during the training programme.

Section 1, Making contact, outlines the approach taken by the training. It stresses that the work is developed from the particular circumstances surrounding each individual, 'there was no such thing as a typical intervention'. It goes on to outline six elements of the work. One of the elements, gaining the individual's attention, is the theme of Section 2. Caldwell uses a series of examples to illustrate ways of claiming the attention of someone with profound and multiple disabilities; for example, she may join in and imitate a person's self-stimulating and repetitive behaviour. In doing this she makes external a stimulus that someone is used to giving themselves, so directing that person's attention to the outside world. She also describes ways of using surprise to divert attention from someone's self-injuring behaviour towards shared activities.

Section 3 looks at ways in which making personalised equipment can help support workers and individuals with learning disabilities to get to know each other.

Section 4, Getting in touch and sharing feelings, describes ways in which some people have become estranged from communication through circular speech patterns and behaviours which are labelled as dysfunctional or disturbed. Section 5, Working at an appropriate level, illustrates the tension between underestimating and overestimating a person's abilities. It identifies different levels of work and looks at how to sustain and build activities beyond individual claiming of attention. Caldwell stresses the need to look for something that interests a person so much that they respond and this can then be built into an activity that can be shared. She argues that it is essential to understand what the behaviour is doing for the individual: our behaviours help us to deal with our worlds.

Section 6 looks at the changes that have resulted from these interventions and contains feedback from experienced support staff. It also touches on how these interventions have changed the ways support staff view the people they work with. Section 7 contains a bullet point checklist of key issues in designing and using equipment, and recalls examples of how they were used during the course. It includes a list of common materials used. In her conclusion, Caldwell says her book is about 'learning to identify and use the languages of people whose often extreme support needs have excluded them from ordinary interactions and shared activities'.

The book is clearly written with summaries of each section and examples of work with particular individuals. It sets out the underlying pattern of Caldwell's approach so that it could be taken up by other support staff with a minimum of training. The book will help staff and supporters to examine the ways they communicate with people with profound and multiple disabilities, and provides a structured approach with which to develop new forms of communication.

Going by bus

FORMAT: Booklet, 40-pages, illustrated
AUDIENCE: People with learning disabilities
PRICE: £3.55 + p&p
PRODUCER: Leeds: PRU Publications, 1994
DISTRIBUTOR: Avanti Books
This booklet is intended to be a 'first reader' for people with learning disabilities. It is a photographic record of a journey by bus from a hostel to the library. On the left side of each double page are two or three simple text sentences in large print that relate to the black-and-white photographs on the right hand page.
The author created the booklet for people attending Basic Education Classes within Social Services day centres in Leeds. People with learning disabilities are shown in all the pictures, going from their group home by bus to the library and choosing a cassette tape to borrow. The author has presented the different aspects of the journey in small, clear stages. The booklet could usefully be used to support sessions about learning to use public transport and making use of community facilities. The photographs do not show anyone using a wheelchair and the booklet does not address the inaccessibility of most public transport for wheelchair users.

Going into hospital

FORMAT: Book, 76-pages, illustrated
AUDIENCE: People with learning disabilities, primary healthcare teams, hospital staff, parents, carers, support workers
AUTHOR: Hollins, S., Avis, A., Cheverton, S. and Redmond, D. (illustrator)
PRICE: £10.00 inc.
PRODUCER: London: Gaskell and St George's Hospital Medical School, 1998
DISTRIBUTOR: Royal College of Psychiatrists, Book Sales
ISBN: 1 901242 19 6
This colour picture book is one of the *Books beyond words* series for people with learning disabilities. It was written by a psychiatrist, a physiotherapist, and a senior nursing sister.
The 54 illustrations tell the story of two people who go into hospital. The aim is to help people with learning disabilities understand the process of going to hospital. There is no text and readers are encouraged to tell the story in their own words. However, simple words matched to each picture are provided at the end of the book for those who prefer a ready-made storyline.
The first story is about Martin, who goes into hospital for a planned operation, and the second story is about Mary, who is admitted as an emergency. The clear, expressive pictures show what happens to Martin and Mary in hospital. These cover routine and medical procedures, such as being admitted, having your blood pressure taken and stitches removed, having an X-ray, ECG, chest examination, anaesthetic, and urine test. Mary is given medicine to take home and a spacer to help her breathe. As well as providing information, the story also explores how Martin and Mary feel about the experience and shows Martin giving his consent to an operation.
Both the main characters are white, although the hospital staff include people from black and minority ethnic groups. The pictures may be accessible to people with partial sight.
The book can support people with learning disabilities who have to go into hospital. Someone with limited reading skills could use the book on their own although they would need help with the medical terms used and additional information about their particular illness and the treatment they need. The medical

terms are explained in simple language in a glossary at the back. Alternatively, a supporter could discuss the story with the patient prior to admission. There is a guide for supporters/informants that covers planned and emergency admissions, and some ideas for using the book. Supporters are advised to contact the hospital before a planned admission to discuss any special needs, to find out more about the hospital, and to arrange a pre-admission visit to the ward with the patient.

The book could also help hospital staff understand the needs of people with learning disabilities and improve communication with them. The pictures show hospital staff using the book with patients before and during treatment. There is a short guide for hospital staff that includes a definition of learning disability and highlights key points about relating to patients with learning disabilities. The guide explains how to use the book to augment communication, and explores the issue of consent.

At the back there is a list of useful resources and organisations. Funding was provided by the Department of Health.

Going to court

FORMAT: Book, 70-pages, illustrated
AUDIENCE: Young people and adults with learning disabilities
AUTHOR: Hollins, S., Sinason, V., Boniface, J. and Webb, B. (illustrator)
PRICE: £10.00 inc.
PRODUCER: London: St George's Hospital Medical School, 1994
DISTRIBUTOR: Royal College of Psychiatrists, Book Sales
ISBN: 1 874439 08 7

This colour picture book was written by a psychiatrist, a psychotherapist, and a parent and manager of Voice (UK), an organisation that helps people with learning disabilities go to court. It is part of the *Books beyond words* series for people with learning disabilities.

The 32 illustrations tell the story of a woman who is a witness in a crown court, in clear and expressive pictures. Readers are encouraged to tell the story in their own words. The pictures suit any crime and any verdict. There is a blank page between each of the pictures where people can draw their own pictures or add their own words if they wish. Words for each page are included at the end of the book for those who prefer a ready-made story.

The story follows Anita, who thinks a man has done something wrong. A friend calls the police who take a statement. Later, Anita goes to court to give evidence. The pictures show the court's procedure, and Anita answering both defending and prosecuting barristers. She feels confused and upset when faced with the questions from the man's barrister. The jury gives its verdict, but the story does not say which way it decided.

The book also includes a glossary giving simple definitions of the roles of those involved in a trial, such as 'prosecutor' or 'usher'. It also gives details of the aims of Voice (UK).

Going to court could be used by someone alone who had limited reading skills or be read with someone. The pictures are very powerful and facial expressions and colour vividly convey feelings. It could be used by both adults and children as the visual imagery is so clear – there are no distracting details, just strong colour and expressive body language. It could be used with people who are going to court or who have already been, either to prepare them or help them make sense of their experience. Facilitators are reminded not to coach witnesses, and that what a witness says in court must be in his or her own words. The characters vary in age and ethnic background.

Going to the doctor

FORMAT: Book, 73-pages, illustrated
AUDIENCE: Young people and adults with learning disabilities, primary healthcare teams
AUTHOR: Hollins, S., Bernal, J. and Gregory, M.
PRICE: £10.00 inc.
PRODUCER: London: St George's Hospital Mental Health Library, 1996
DISTRIBUTOR: Royal College of Psychiatrists, Book Sales
ISBN: 1 874439 13 3

This colour picture book is part of the *Books beyond words* series for people with learning disabilities. It is designed to be used alongside a support worker with the aim of explaining some common events when visiting the doctor.

The pack begins with Jim and Ann arriving at a health centre. It then illustrates, in clear and expressive pictures, six possible scenarios that might occur during a visit to the doctor. Readers are encouraged to tell the story in their own words. Text for each picture is included at the end for those who prefer a ready-made story. The pictures show Jim, an elderly white man, and Ann, a younger white woman, checking in at the surgery or health centre and sitting in the waiting room, each reading *Going to the doctor* with their support workers. A doctor calls one of them and sits down to listen to their needs or explain what is going to happen. Section 1, Something odd happens, shows Jim having his blood pressure checked; in section 2, Something embarrassing happens, the doctor examines Jim's stomach; in section 3, Something hurts, the doctor gives Jim an injection; section 4, Something makes me better, shows Ann having her ears syringed by a nurse; in section 5, Something pricks, Ann has a blood test; in the final scenario, Something to make me better, the doctor writes a prescription for Ann. Each scenario uses seven or eight pictures showing the doctor or nurse explaining the intervention, using *Going to the doctor.* These pictures can be used to obtain the patient's consent. There is plenty of detail to help explore how people might feel about each intervention. It is suggested that facilitators always start with the introductory pictures showing Jim and Ann arriving at the health centre, and then choose the scenario that is most similar to the procedure which is planned. The guidance notes for support workers recommend that the pack be used both before a visit to the doctor and in the surgery itself. It could also be used in more general health education work with individuals or groups to talk about experiences of primary health care in order to reduce anxiety.

The pictures are powerful, and the facial expressions and colour vividly convey feelings. It could be used by both adults and children as the visual imagery is so clear – there are no distracting details, just strong colour and expressive body language. A glossary explains medical words, such as blood pressure, ear syringe, injection, etc., in simple language. The final section is a guide for general practitioners and the primary care team, which includes a definition of learning disability and a discussion about the issue of consent, stressing the importance of working with support workers and of using augmentative communication where appropriate. This section also suggests appropriate forms of health surveillance and health promotion for people with learning disabilities, including routine checks necessary for people with Down's syndrome. The pack ends with a list of useful resources, including a description of the role of community teams for people with a learning disability, and the addresses of learning disability organisations.

Going to out-patients

FORMAT: Book, 61-pages, illustrated
AUDIENCE: People with learning disabilities, hospital staff, supporters
AUTHOR: Hollins, S., Bernal, J., Gregory, M. and Redmond, D. (illustrator)
PRICE: £10.00 inc.
PRODUCER: London: Gaskell and St. George's Hospital Medical School, 1998
DISTRIBUTOR: Royal College of Psychiatrists, Book Sales
ISBN: 1 901242 18 8
This colour picture book is one of the *Books beyond words* series for people with learning disabilities. It was written by two psychiatrists and a senior nurse and is dedicated to the memory of Veronica Donaghy, an editorial adviser.
The 39 illustrations tell the story of Bill Banks, Jane Gunn, and Anna Lee who attend out-patient appointments. The pictures explain what happens to them and cover routine procedures as well as medical tests and treatment. There is no text and readers are encouraged to tell the story in their own words. However, simple words matched to each picture are provided at the end of the book for those who prefer a ready-made storyline. The story is broken down into a number of events that are clearly separated by colour dividers with different colours for each patient.
In the first section, the three of them arrive at the hospital. In the next two sections Jane Gunn meets the doctor and has an ultrasound. Bill Banks then meets the doctor and has an X-ray and plaster cast for his broken arm. The last two sections tell the story of Anna Lee, who meets the ear, nose, and throat doctor and has a hearing test. In the different scenarios, the three characters are shown considering whether to give their consent to the tests. The people illustrated come from a range of black and minority ethnic groups and the clarity of the pictures may make this book accessible to some partially sighted people.
The book could be read by someone with limited reading skills, although they would need help with the medical terms used and any additional information relevant to their illness and the treatment they need. A glossary of medical terms is provided. Alternatively, a supporter could select the most appropriate storyline to discuss with the patient prior to an out-patient visit, and there are brief notes on how to use this resource.
The book could also help hospital staff understand the needs of people with learning disabilities and improve communication with them. There is a short guide for hospital staff which includes a definition of learning disability and highlights some key points about relating to patients with learning disabilities. The guide explains how the book can be used to augment communication and explores the issue of consent.
At the back there is a list of useful resources and organisations. Funding was provided by the Department of Health.

Habit families

FORMAT: Pack – A6, colour, illustrated; A6 postcards (x30); A4 sheets (x2)
AUDIENCE: Young people with learning disabilities, teachers, support workers
AUTHOR: Ives, R.
PRICE: £40.00 inc. VAT
PRODUCER: London: Richard Ives, 1995
DISTRIBUTOR: Richard Ives
This pack is designed to provide an easy and safe way of discussing drugs and can be used in conjunction with the larger pack *Special needs and drug education*, available from the same author and reviewed in this publication. It can be used

by those with experience of working with young people with learning disabilities, either in schools or in youth and community settings, preferably as part of a continuing drugs education programme. The pack aims to promote positive images of people with learning disabilities.
The pack consists of a card game, instructions for playing, and a photocopy sheet of the card set. There are 30 laminated cards with colour pictures of a range of substances that can be ingested. Instructions are provided for playing seven games, with brief notes for facilitators. Some information and guidance is provided for those with less experience of working with this audience. It is designed to be flexible for use with a wide range of teaching groups. Games can be modified by selecting cards. The pack was developed as part of a project funded by Hackney Drugs Prevention Team in London.

Healthy eating and exercise

FORMAT: Booklet, 10-pages
AUDIENCE: Young people and adults with Down's syndrome
AUTHOR: Sawtell, M.
PRICE: 50p inc.
PRODUCER: London: Down's Syndrome Association, 1993
DISTRIBUTOR: Down's Syndrome Association
This booklet gives an overview of why healthy eating and exercise are important for young people and adults with Down's syndrome. It is intended to be read by people with Down's syndrome with support from families or professionals. It consists entirely of text and is set out as a series of questions, such as 'Is it more common for a person with Down's syndrome to be overweight?' or 'Can being underweight be a problem?' Some of the language is complex, though medical terms used are clearly explained.
It looks at what factors may be responsible for a person with Down's syndrome being overweight, including possible links with a slower than average basal metabolic rate, boredom leading to overeating and underactivity, physical factors, and medical factors such as thyroid disorders. The leaflet cites social and medical reasons why extra weight gain should be avoided and suggests ways that this can be achieved. Facts to remember about exercise and control of calories are set out as bullet points – for example, 'The way to get fitter is to be more vigorous than you usually are' or 'Fibre is also good for you as it makes you feel full and helps to prevent constipation, which can be a problem for people with Down's syndrome.'
A brief description of what makes up a healthy diet is given, including details of the four main food groups, with an emphasis on reducing fat and sugar in the diet. Seven cheap and fast meals are listed, such as jacket potato with a low fat filling or shish kebabs in pitta bread with salad. There is a 'Useful tips' section providing suggestions such as keeping a food diary and making a shopping list which you stick to. The booklet finishes with a list of people from whom to seek help, such as general practitioners, health visitors, or sports coaches, and a suggested reading list which includes material about healthy eating, exercise, and medical information for parents and carers.

HIV and learning disability

FORMAT: Book, 186-pages
AUDIENCE: Professionals working in the field of HIV and learning disability
AUTHOR: Cambridge, P. and Brown, H. (eds.)
PRICE: £20.00 + p&p
PRODUCER: Kidderminster: British Institute of Learning Disabilities (BILD), 1997

DISTRIBUTOR: BILD Publications, Plymbridge Distributors
This book aims to provide reference material for people working in the field of HIV and learning disability, including recommendations for sex education. The book contains 11 chapters, each written by a different author.
Chapter 1 looks at assessing and responding to local need, and argues for the re-gaying of HIV and AIDS in services for people with learning disabilities. It explores the organisational context in which needs are recognised and services and resources are commissioned. It suggests pointers for best practice and gives an overview of the options for service. Chapter 2 provides a factual explanation of the transmission, virology, and treatment of HIV infection and AIDS.
Chapter 3 looks at the role of health promotion services in co-ordinating local initiatives. It reviews models of health promotion and argues for a multi-agency approach, grounded in the reality of risk.
Chapter 4 is written by a service provider and describes work with one man in a residential service who is at high risk of HIV infection. It looks at the implications for planning and delivering services and considers the impact on staff culture.
Chapter 5 describes safer sex work with men with learning disabilities who have sex with men. Chapter 6 focuses on HIV and heterosexual sex and looks at some of the practical aspects of sex education with individuals and in groups.
Chapter 7 describes the role of therapy in sexual health, placing HIV and AIDS in the context of other threats and risks faced by people with learning disabilities.
Chapter 8 shows how people with learning disabilities can be empowered to make sexual choices and to understand HIV and AIDS. It focuses on methods that use visual images and peer education to develop self-advocacy about safer sex and relationships. Chapter 9 looks at the potential of sex education with younger people with learning disabilities. Written by a head teacher, it describes work in a special school in Nottingham which involved children, parents, and other interest groups. It looks at how to support sex education as part of the school curriculum. Chapter 10 addresses four specific legal issues which are of potential concern to services, advocates, and supporters: testing, criminal liability for the spread of HIV infection, legal issues surrounding the disclosure of someone's HIV status, and compulsory powers under 'AIDS legislation'. The responsibilities that services have for providing competent support for people at risk of HIV are explained. The final chapter outlines the contribution policies can make in the area of HIV and learning disability and sets out the pros and cons of written guidelines.
As the introduction makes clear, the book has a clear practice bias and draws on the experiences of successful services and practitioners. It will be a useful resource for those who need to explore issues of HIV and learning disability in depth. By providing an assessment of competence in responding to HIV, it will also enable service providers to evaluate the range of services they offer. The book is clearly set out and contains an index of the issues it covers. Most of the chapters include bullet point summaries of the key points. The book contains a lot of detail and draws on a wealth of experience. It is particularly strong in addressing issues of power, control, exploitation, and abuse.

HIV and AIDS and people with learning disabilities. A guide for parents

FORMAT: Booklet, 8-pages
AUDIENCE: Parents
AUTHOR: Cambridge, P.
PRICE: £2.50 (single) or £7.50 for the set of 3 in this series
PRODUCER: Kidderminster: British Institute of Learning Disabilities (BILD), 1996
DISTRIBUTOR: BILD Publications, Plymbridge Distributors

This booklet, written by a lecturer at the Tizard Centre, is one of a series of three entitled *HIV and AIDS and people with learning disabilities*. These booklets update and revise an earlier series, *AIDS and people with learning difficulties*, originally written in 1991. The new edition, published in 1995, makes changes to take into account current terminology, attitudes, priorities, and knowledge about AIDS and HIV.

This booklet provides information on HIV/AIDS for parents of people with learning disabilities. The introduction acknowledges the dilemmas parents face in trying to find a balance between concern for their children and their son's or daughter's own needs for privacy and personal development. It reassures parents at the same time as making a strong argument for planned sex education programmes that give people with learning disabilities the information they need to avoid abuse and exploitation, and the language to express their own sexual preferences, feelings, and experiences.

The remainder of the booklet uses a question and answer format. There are 10 questions and each answer is about a paragraph in length. The questions raised are: What are HIV and AIDS?; How is HIV transmitted?; What is safer sex?; Are there other ways to reduce risk?; Who is most at risk?; How does HIV affect people with learning disabilities?; Is my son or daughter at risk?; What can services do?; Do I need to take precautions?; and What can I do?

The booklet contains text with no pictures. The answers are written clearly and simply, although some terms may need further explanation, such as a reference to AZT. It ends with three contact addresses for further information – The Terrence Higgins Trust, London People First and the Health Education Authority.

The booklet could be a valuable introduction for parents who may be concerned that their son or daughter is at risk or who may have concerns about the relevance of sex education programmes. However, it is likely to raise as many questions as it answers and so it is important that parents have access to someone who will be able to give further advice or information about HIV and AIDS.

The other booklets in the series are *What you need to know about HIV and AIDS* (for people with learning disabilities) and *Guide for staff and carers.*

HIV and AIDS and people with learning disabilities. Guide for staff and carers

FORMAT: Booklet, 20-pages
AUDIENCE: Support staff and carers
AUTHOR: Cambridge, P.
PRICE: £3.00 (single); £7.50 for the set of 3 in the series
PRODUCER: Kidderminster: British Institute of Learning Disabilities (BILD), 1996
DISTRIBUTOR: BILD Publications, Plymbridge Distributors

This booklet, written by a lecturer at the Tizard Centre, is one of a series of three entitled, *HIV and AIDS and people with learning disabilities*. These booklets update and revise an earlier series, *AIDS and people with learning difficulties*, originally written in 1991. The new edition, published in 1995, makes changes to take into account current terminology, attitudes, priorities, and knowledge about HIV and AIDS.

This booklet for staff and carers provides information about HIV and the importance of sex education for people with learning disabilities. The introduction sets HIV and AIDS in the context of broader political and sex education issues. It emphasises the importance of making information available to people with learning disabilities to enable them to make more informed choices. It summarises the service philosophies surrounding community care and outlines the rights that people with learning disabilities should have in their lives as a whole and in respect of their personal relationships.

The next section presents basic information about HIV and AIDS in a question and answer format. There are 13 questions and each answer is about a paragraph in length. The questions raised are: What is HIV?; How is HIV transmitted?; What does HIV do?; What happens to people infected by HIV?; What is AIDS?; Can HIV and AIDS be treated?; Who is most at risk?; Does safer sex education work?; What is safer sex?; What is high and low risk?; What other ways can people avoid HIV infection?; To test or not to test?; Is HIV a risk at work? The answers go into more medical detail than the similar sections in the other two booklets in the series. The answers are clearly written, using text without pictures.

The following section looks briefly at some of the central issues in HIV/AIDS education with people with learning disabilities. It outlines the key messages contained in the booklet for people with learning disabilities, and reminds staff and carers that these messages are simplifications (e.g. not mentioning the risk of transmission by vaginal fluids) and that they may want to include infomation about other low risk activities (e.g. from vaginal fluids in oral sex). The booklet stresses the importance of sex education and the need for co-ordinated and consistent reponses and interventions. It highlights issues of confidentiality, the need to take account of policies and guidelines, and to work in parallel with carers, support workers, and parents.

The booklet is a useful starting point for carers and workers. Those intending to undertake HIV/AIDS education as part of a planned programme will need further information, and the comprehensive list of resources at the end of the booklet will be invaluable. This list is very thorough and includes information on videos, packs, leaflets, booklets, teaching aids, reference books, staff training materials, and contact addresses.

The other booklets in the series are *What you need to know about HIV and AIDS* (for people with learning disabilities) and *A Guide for parents*.

HIV and AIDS and people with learning disabilities. What you need to know about HIV and AIDS

FORMAT: Booklet, 16-pages, illustrated
AUDIENCE: People with learning disabilities
AUTHOR: Cambridge, P.
PRICE: £3.50 (single); £7.50 for the set of 3 in this series
PRODUCER: Kidderminster: British Institute of Learning Disabilities (BILD), 1996
DISTRIBUTOR: BILD Publications, Plymbridge Distributors
This booklet, written by a lecturer at the Tizard Centre, is one of a series of three entitled, *HIV and AIDS and people with learning disabilities*. These booklets update and revise an earlier series, *AIDS and people with learning difficulties*, originally written in 1991. The new edition, published in 1995, includes changes to take account of current terminology, attitudes, priorities, and knowledge about AIDS and HIV.
What you need to know about HIV and AIDS is aimed at people with learning disabilities. It uses large text, brief sentences, and full colour drawings. Each page deals with a different issue. The areas covered are: What is HIV and AIDS?; How do people get HIV and AIDS?; Sex and HIV; HIV and injecting drugs; Safer sex; Saying no is OK; Being clean; Cleaning up; Meeting someone; and Living together. As well as giving an explanation of AIDS and guidelines around safer sex, the booklet sets HIV and AIDS in a wider context, with pages on personal hygiene, relationships, and saying no. It ends with a summary of the key messages. These messages and the information contained in the booklet as a whole are necessarily simplifications. For example, the risk of transmission by vaginal fluids is not mentioned. Support workers may want to include infomation about other low risk activities, for example from vaginal fluids in oral sex.
The pictures are clear, showing characters from different ethnic backgrounds and of different ages. The gender of the characters is ambiguous so the couples shown could be gay or heterosexual. The booklet could be used by someone on their own who has reading skills, or be read with a support worker, parent, or carer. It could also be used in group work. The language is necessarily explicit and it would need to be used with people who have already had some sex education and preferably in the context of a wider sex education programme.
The other booklets in the series are *A guide for parents* and *Guide for staff and carers*.

HIV, sex and learning disability

FORMAT: Pack, 252 pages, illustrated
AUDIENCE: Professionals, support workers, men with learning disabilities who have sex with men
AUTHOR: Cambridge, P.
PRICE: £115.00
PRODUCER: Brighton: Pavilion Publishing, 1997
DISTRIBUTOR: Pavilion Publishing Ltd
ISBN: 1 900600 61 7
This resource was developed for use with a range of staff, including support workers, residential managers, commissioners, and health promotion specialists. It provides a flexible range of educational materials designed for working on HIV and AIDS with learning disabled people and, in particular, men with learning disabilities who have sex with men.

One of the aims of this pack is to have a positive effect on the lives and well-being of learning disabled men and other people involved with them. The author, a gay man, stresses that it does not set out to replace other resources that have a wider application, but seeks to address openly and honestly the issues of homosexuality, HIV, and AIDS, subjects that are marginalised in our heterosexual culture.
The manual is in two parts. Part 1 contains staff training exercises, designed to help participants understand HIV and AIDS, and some exercises will highlight prejudice. There are examples of training programmes and information about help-lines and other organisations.
Part 2 consists of sex education resources. These include record sheets to assist in the identification of individual needs, photocopiable drawings, and a range of prompt symbols to aid communication. These materials, with enlargement, may be accessible to some people with partial sight. The drawings are explicit and there is guidance on their use. The illustrations are designed to convey key messages; for example, that sexuality, consenting sex, and safer sex can be good, but that unpleasant and bad things can happen. The drawings include people from black and minority ethnic groups. Cultural and personal differences are upheld by equal opportunities principles that avoid sexism, homophobia, and racism.
Careful targeting of these materials is important and they should be matched to the needs of the user. An experienced sex educator might be the person best equipped to deliver them. They should not be used outside a broader appreciation of sexuality and learning disability, or without reference to wider service implications. There are suggestions about how the two parts can be used separately and flexibly with individuals or in groups.

The Department of Health funded this pack and the exercises have been piloted and developed in a variety of settings.

Home cooking

FORMAT: Multi-media – instructors' guide, 81-pages, illustrated; A4 looseleaf sheets (x38); A4 resource file, illustrated; looseleaf sheets (x1), supplemental recipes; recipe set, 56-pages, illustrated; coloured tape (x5); marker pen; pencil; eraser
AUDIENCE: People with learning disabilities
AUTHOR: Sudol, E.
PRICE: £99.95 + VAT + 12% p&p
PRODUCER: USA: Attainment Company, 1994
DISTRIBUTOR: Winslow Press
The Home Cooking recipe set contains a range of savoury and sweet recipes. Methods for cooking each recipe are set out in colourful picture sequences making them much easier to follow than ordinary cookery books. Each recipe is laminated and can be taken out of the clip file to be used in the kitchen. The recipes are designed for oven, microwave, and hob. There are also some cold recipes such as salads and sandwiches.
The complexity of the recipes varies from jacket potatoes to hamburgers. For people with more experience, 'meal plans' are included to help with timing the cooking of more than one item – for example, 'chicken with mashed potatoes and carrots'. The picture sequences mean that the resource can be used by people without reading skills, although it may be necessary to read it through with them first.
An accompanying guide for facilitators gives common-sense guidelines on using the recipes and sets out learning objectives and teaching suggestions. There is also a monitoring form to help facilitators record individual progress and a system of colour coding which some people may find

helpful for measuring quantities and temperature.
The resource was produced in the USA, so names for some ingredients differ from those used in the UK (for example, *zucchini* is used for courgette); and some ingredients (for example, squash) may not be familiar or easily obtainable. However, these recipes can be easily adapted.

How can I make a complaint?

FORMAT: Video, 15 mins
AUDIENCE: People with learning disabilities
PRICE: £28.00 inc.; £25.00 to advocacy groups
PRODUCER: Rotherham: Speakup Self Advocacy, 1995
DISTRIBUTOR: Speakup Self Advocacy
This video is one of a series produced by SpeakUp, a self-advocacy group in Rotherham. Other titles in the series include: *How to go into hospital*, *What can I do if I'm arrested?* and *Living safely*. It aims to help people with learning difficulties make a complaint and would be useful to advocates and those supporting people with learning difficulties. The video would also be of interest to self-advocacy groups, day centres, colleges, residential homes, or any other centre or group.
The video follows the story of David – a young man who attends a day centre and wants to change the group he is in because he doesn't get on with the others. He speaks to a day centre worker and the centre manager, both of whom tell him why he cannot change groups. David then speaks to a friend who tells him there is a complaints officer in social services he can contact. We see David writing to and being visited by the Complaints Officer, who recommends that his case should be heard by another centre manager. David's complaint isn't upheld and the complaints officer tells him that he can take the matter to local councillors. David meets the councillors and is questioned by them. A few days later the Complaints Officer visits David again to tell him that the decision has been reversed and he will be allowed to change groups after all.
The video is very clear and easy to follow. The pace is slow without being too slow, and one main idea is explored. Important points are repeated and there are natural breaks in between scenes to enable facilitators to stop the video and check understanding before moving on to the next section. Many people with learning disabilities will be able to access the information without needing to watch it with a facilitator. However, for others it would be useful to watch the video with someone who can reinforce the message and talk through issues such as how someone who can't read and write can contact the complaints officer.
At the end of David's story, a voice-over explains that if you have a complaint the first step is to speak to the people concerned. If the complaint is not resolved then you may wish to make an official complaint. If it is a serious complaint an advocate may be able to assist you. The video shows a number of other people with learning disabilities speaking about complaints they made with varying degrees of success. Some of these complaints were serious, some were not, and some could not be solved by anyone – for example, one woman complained about the fact it rained on their sports day. This section of the video could be used as a trigger for discussion or role-play around the types of complaints people might want to make, how serious the complaints are, and whether they are things that people can help with or not. All of the people featured in the video are adults and all are white.

How to go into hospital

FORMAT: Video, 15 mins
AUDIENCE: People with learning disabilities
PRICE: £25.00 (advocacy groups) £28.00 (other groups)
PRODUCER: Rotherham: Speakup Self Advocacy, 1995
DISTRIBUTOR: Speakup Self Advocacy
This video shows Gladys going into hospital for an operation. It aims to help people with learning disabilities to understand what happens when they go into hospital. The video is one of a series produced by Speakup, a self-advocacy group in Rotherham. Other titles in the series include *What can I do if I'm arrested?* and *Living safely*. All of the videos are devised by people with learning disabilities and aim to make information more accessible.
How to go into hospital begins as Gladys, a 60-year-old woman with a learning disability, leaves her house to go into hospital for an operation on her neck. The remainder of the video is a step-by-step guide showing what can happen when you go into hospital. Gladys is shown travelling to hospital in a taxi, meeting her support worker, checking in with the admissions clerk, finding her ward, meeting her 'named nurse' and having an initial check-up and blood test.
Gladys's exchanges with hospital staff are shown at length, giving the viewer time to understand the kinds of questions that could be asked. A voice-over (by a person with a learning disability) explains why there are so many questions for Gladys to answer and gives further information about hospital procedures. The video ends as Gladys is shown her bed, and a voice-over tells us that 'Gladys was in hospital for four days ... she quite enjoyed it although she didn't like the food'. All the participants in the video are white, and the hospital staff involved play themselves.
The video would be a useful tool to inform individuals or groups about what to expect when going into hospital, both in terms of their contact with hospital staff and the basic check-ups (blood pressure, pulse, temperature, blood test) they are likely to have. Although no clear pause points are indicated on screen, each step in the process could be used to trigger further discussion, particularly about the feelings people might experience when going into hospital. The overall tone of the video is both informative and reassuring.

Hug me, touch me

FORMAT: Book, 70-pages, illustrated
AUDIENCE: Young people and adults with learning disabilities
AUTHOR: Hollins, S., Roth, T. and Webb, B. (illustrator)
PRICE: £10.00 inc.
PRODUCER: London: St George's Hospital Medical Library, 1994
DISTRIBUTOR: Royal College of Psychiatrists, Book Sales
ISBN: 1 874439 05 2
This colour picture book was written by a psychiatrist and a clinical psychologist and is part of the *Books beyond words* series for people with learning disabilities.
The 33 illustrations tell a story about appropriate touching from a woman's perspective. *Making friends* (p.96) tells a similar story from a man's perspective. The pictures are clear and expressive, and readers are encouraged to tell the story in their own words. There is blank page between each of the pictures where people can draw their own pictures if they wish. Words for each page are included at the end of the book for those who prefer a ready-made story.
The story follows a young woman who goes for a walk in a park. In an attempt to

be friendly, she tries to hug a baby who is with its mother, to play with some children, and to hug a pair of lovers. In each case, she is rejected by these people who are all strangers. Hurt and upset, the woman goes home and telephones a friend. The friend comes round, listens, hugs, and comforts her. The two friends then go out together and meet people they know. They all greet each other appropriately and the main character goes home happy and reflects upon what she has learned about touching. The main character is white, her friend is black, and the other characters are from a range of ethnic groups.

The book could be used alone by someone who has limited reading skills or be read with someone. The pictures are very powerful and facial expressions and colour vividly convey feelings. It could be used by both adults and children as the visual imagery is so clear – there are no distracting details, just strong colour and expressive body language. It could be used with groups or individuals to explore appropriate greeting and touch between people, and would fit well in a programme of social skills education.

I'm a person not a label

FORMAT: Video, 16 mins
AUDIENCE: People with learning disabilities, advocacy groups
PRICE: £25.00 + £1.99 p&p (statutory organisations); £15.00 + £1.99 p&p (voluntary and advocacy groups)
PRODUCER: Manchester: People First, 1994
DISTRIBUTOR: Manchester People First

This video was made by a group of people with learning disabilities who belong to a self-advocacy group in Manchester. Three members of the group (two men and one woman, all of whom are white) talk about their interests and the things they do with their time – birdwatching, plane watching, and helping out in a local pub. They speak of the discrimination people with learning disabilities face, and interview members of the public about what they understand by the term 'learning difficulty'.

The video's central message is that people with learning disabilities are coming together to speak out and take control of their own lives. Members of a self-advocacy group talk about their experiences of being attacked and pestered by neighbours, being called names, bad experiences of living in institutions in the past, home life, and school. They express their outrage and their support for each other; these experiences are seen as an issue of civil rights and members of the group argue that they must stand up for their rights.

The video also includes a development worker for North Manchester Self-Advocacy, who describes her work supporting people with learning disabilities in developing self-advocacy skills. A short section looks at the work of Manchester People First and some of the organisational tasks that need to be performed. The video ends with the three main presenters saying that this video is their contribution to raising awareness about the rights of people with learning disabilities; they challenge the viewer to contribute something too.

This video will be of interest to self-advocacy groups and those interested in setting up or joining self-advocacy groups to give them a sense of what such a group can be like. It could also be used to raise political awareness or as part of disability equality training with people with learning disabilities and others.

I can get through it

FORMAT: Book, 44-pages, illustrated
AUDIENCE: Women with learning disabilities who have been abused
AUTHOR: Hollins, S., Horrocks, C., Sinason, V. and Kopper, L. (illustrator)
PRICE: £10.00 inc.
PRODUCER: London: Gaskell and St George's Hospital Medical School, 1998
DISTRIBUTOR: Royal College of Psychiatrists, Book Sales
ISBN: 1 901242 20 X
This colour picture book is one of the *Books beyond words* series for people with learning disabilities. It was written by a psychiatrist, a psychotherapist, and a Director of Voice (UK). The Department of Health funded the publication.
The 34 illustrations tell the story of Susie, a woman with learning disabilities who is abused. The book explains that help is available for people who suffer abuse. There is no text and readers are encouraged to tell the story in their own words. However, simple words matched to each expressive picture are provided at the end of the book for those who prefer a ready-made storyline. There are blank pages facing some of the illustrations where people could draw their own pictures or add their own words. Smaller drawings are used opposite some of the pictures to tell parts of the story.
In this book, Susie's life is dramatically disturbed by an incidence of abuse in the home where she lives. At the beginning, Susie is shown enjoying herself but following the abuse one night she becomes very angry and upset. She cannot sleep and keeps remembering the man who came into her room. No one can understand what has happened until she sees a counsellor. After several visits, Susie draws pictures and uses dolls to show the counsellor what happened. With the counsellor's support Susie tells the police and the man is arrested. Gradually memories of the abuse fade and Susie starts to enjoy life again with the help of her home and friends.
The majority of the characters are white. The clear illustrations may be accessible to people with partial sight.
The book needs to be used sensitively, and anyone using it should have the expertise to deal with revelations of abuse. Before using the book, supporters and professionals will need to prepare the reader and consider follow-up work. It would be helpful to know about support networks available. At the back of the book there are more detailed notes about the type of treatment available for people with learning disabilities who have been abused and how help can be obtained. There is a list of useful resources and organisations including a description of Voice (UK), a support and information group for people with learning disabilities who have been abused.

Independent living skills

FORMAT: Video pack – video, 40 mins; notes, 110-pages, illustrated
AUDIENCE: Young people with disabilities (15 to 25 years old), teachers, youth workers, support workers
AUTHOR: Greater Manchester Coalition of Disabled People
PRICE: £65.00 + VAT; £35.00 + VAT for disabled people's groups
PRODUCER: Brighton: Pavilion Publishing Ltd, 1998
DISTRIBUTOR: Pavilion Publishing Ltd
This training pack aims to encourage young disabled people to think about independence in its widest form, as choice, control, and power over their own lives.
The central message is that disabled people are powerful and resourceful and have similar expectations of life to everyone else.

The pack was made by the Manchester Coalition of Disabled People with funding from The Joseph Rowntree Foundation. The target audience is young disabled people between the ages of 15 and 25 years. The emphasis in the workbook is on people with physical disabilities, male and female, from different black and minority ethnic groups. Much of the content will need to be adapted for people with learning disabilities, although the video itself offers encouraging role models. The training course is designed for use by facilitators working with small groups of young disabled people. It assumes a basic awareness of disability rights issues, training, and course organisation. The programme is underpinned by the social care model of disability and aims to empower people through information, discussion, and consciousness-raising exercises. There are 20 session modules that break down into four sections: Personal development, which includes disability awareness; Employment; Transport; and Independent living. The working is not prescriptive but provides examples of work done, together with handouts and exercises that have worked well with the participants concerned. The video was made by the young participants from the course and demonstrates the process of the sessions with many positive examples and feedback from individuals about their own lives and experiences. It is intended to be an overview of the issues that matter when young disabled people contemplate independence and puts forward many ideas for further exploration. This pack will provide a good introduction to disability awareness for personal and social education courses in secondary schools, as preparation and inspiration for young people leaving special schools, for general education for youth groups, and as training material for support workers or other social care courses.

The independent travel pack

FORMAT: Multi-media – videos (x3); training manual, 76-pages; personal planners (x6 looseleaf pocket binders); discussion cards (x7); assessment and recording forms; A3 poster, illustrated; learning game
AUDIENCE: Adults with learning and physical disabilities
AUTHOR: Dundee Mental Health Unit
PRICE: £199.00 + VAT; £159 + VAT (voluntary groups)
PRODUCER: Dundee: Dundee Healthcare NHS Trust, 1993
DISTRIBUTOR: Everyday Skills Packs
This package is intended to enable adults with learning disabilities and/or physical disabilities to develop independent travel skills through a thorough, staged system of skills assessment, planning, and review. Training methods used include group work, role-play, travel practice, and the use of videos and games. People with learning disabilities and staff were involved in the pack's design and it reflects this, for example, in the way it takes into account differing literacy levels. It is helpful to have one person, Shona, featured throughout, though it might have been better had she done some or all of the voice-over in the video. Instead, she is spoken for throughout, with continuous and perhaps distracting background music. Shona is a white woman, and the pack has no visual or other references to other ethnic groups. Involvement of people with learning disabilities in planning the programme is generally well addressed – for example, in the initial process of establishing whether or not individuals want to participate. The programme is so comprehensive that it could be overwhelming – for example, there are 18 different assessment and record forms. While each one is clear, well explained and constructive, the cumulative

effect is daunting and would require a committed staff team with the administrative skills and time to manage such a comprehensive programme. However, if staff and participants can cope with the administrative requirements of the pack, they will find it an exceptional resource for travel training, covering all relevant issues including time, money, safety (road and 'stranger danger'), and social interactions. The pack is most likely to be used in adult day services, but would also be useful for carers and teachers of older children and young people, who could adapt it to fit into the National Curriculum.

The cost of the resource may be a barrier to some. However, it could be borrowed or shared between a group of services.

It's my IPP

FORMAT: Video, 15 mins
AUDIENCE: People with learning disabilities
PRICE: £28.00 inc.; £25.00 to advocacy groups
PRODUCER: Rotherham: Speakup Self Advocacy, 1996
DISTRIBUTOR: Speakup Self Advocacy

This video, produced by SpeakUp, a self-advocacy group in Rotherham, looks at Individual Programme Plans (IPPs), what they are, and how people with learning disabilities can gain more control over them. It emphasises the message that 'the IPP is for you'.

The video begins as Fred discusses his IPP with a friend. He's not sure why he has to have one. Several people with learning disabilities give their views to camera on what an IPP is – for example, an IPP is to talk about my needs and for planning my future. The voice-over adds more detail: 'It is your chance to say what you want in the next year, and think about how you are going to do it'.

The rest of the video follows Fred through two IPP meetings – one in which nothing goes the way he wants it (a red border remains on the screen in this scene) and one in which he does make choices for himself (a green border stays on screen). First of all, Fred is shown talking with his key worker who tells him where his IPP meeting will take place, who will be there (after each person is mentioned we see a picture of them on screen), and what is to be discussed. Fred objects to the venue, his parents being there, and the fact that his relationship is on the agenda. His wishes are ignored. The meeting is held at the day centre, chaired by the centre manager, with the main subject of discussion being the worries of professionals and parents about his relationship. Even the woman from the corner shop has been invited and gives her opinion on whether Fred is ready to live in the community. The meeting continues until Fred shouts, 'Stop! It's not my IPP, it's everybody else's'.

The meeting between Fred and his key worker is then replayed. This time, Fred says 'Stop!' whenever he objects to what is being said. He wants the meeting held at his home where he feels more comfortable and asks for his key worker, an advocate, his course tutor, occupational therapist, and centre manager to be there. We then see him phoning to invite these people to the meeting. He objects to the agenda and says he wants to discuss his college course, where he's going to live, and how to make his own coffee in a microwave. Each of these stopping points is reinforced by graphics (e.g. Remember – you can choose who comes to your IPP.) We then see the IPP meeting running as Fred wanted it – he chairs it, the workers listen to him, and enable him to make choices. As Fred says, 'This was my IPP because I planned it.' The video ends with advice about ways to prepare for your IPP: talking it over with someone you trust; using proformas (two are shown on screen) to help you think through what you want; making an audio or video tape about your choices before the meeting; using symbols during the meeting; and having an advocate at the meeting. The video provides a comprehensive look at IPP meetings and presents a positive model of a person with a learning disability achieving what they set out to do and taking control of their own programme planning. It will help people plan their IPP, either in groups or individually. It could also be used to look more generally at assertion skills, or with key workers to explore how to empower people with learning disabilities through the IPP process.

It's only natural

FORMAT: Video pack – video, 25 mins; booklet, 22-pages
AUDIENCE: Parents and carers
PRICE: £70.00 + VAT
PRODUCER: Bradford: Barnardo's Sexual Health Team, 1996
DISTRIBUTOR: Pavilion Publishing Ltd.

This resource was produced for parents, carers, and others involved in the lives of young people with a learning disability. The video and accompanying booklet address the concerns that parents, in particular, may have about their son's and or daughter's sexuality and the growing provision of sexual health and relationship education. It is designed to get the viewer(s) thinking and talking about this difficult subject.

The video tells the story of a group of learning disabled students who attend college classes where sex education appears on the agenda, and illustrates the diverse reactions of the students, their parents, and college staff to this news. There are many conflicting points of view and different ideas. The need to encourage parents to be involved and supportive is highlighted, and the drama illustrates the benefits to all concerned in the long run. Subjects covered include: permission; letting go; vulnerability; sexually transmitted diseases, including HIV and AIDS; self-esteem; and rights and responsibilities. These subjects are touched on very briefly and the booklet suggests that a programme of sex education should include a great deal more and be part of an ongoing process. The booklet does take a more detailed look at some of the issues raised and suggests possible topics for discussion as well as useful contacts.

There are also suggestions about how to use this resource. It can be viewed by parents at home or in a more structured way with groups, either as a 'one-off', or as a framework for a series of approximately 13 workshops. Anyone wishing to facilitate a group should be prepared to address issues and feelings that might arise. The video might be accessible to people with sight difficulties but the lack of introductory information and the small print in the booklet may make it difficult to follow.

The subject of culture and beliefs is dealt with clearly. The pack acknowledges the strong reservations that some people from different cultures and religions may have about the open discussion of sexual matters.

The Barnado's Sexual Health Team produced this pack with funding from Bradford Health Authority. They suggest ways of making contact with useful community resources, and welcome calls for further help and advice.

Jason's private world

FORMAT: Video pack – video 20 mins; notes, 23-pages, illustrated
AUDIENCE: Young men and boys with learning disabilities
PRICE: £50.00 + VAT
PRODUCER: London: Life Support Productions, 1996
DISTRIBUTOR: Life Support Productions

This animated video is intended for use by young men and boys with learning disabilities as part of a general sex education programme. It was developed in response to feedback on an earlier sex education video, *You, your body and sex*. It is accompanied by viewing notes and a resource list.

The pack covers 15 different topics ranging from the physical aspects of sex education (such as body changes from childhood to adult, self-examination, and personal hygiene) to emotional and social dimensions (such as relationships, love, affection, consent, being alone, and dealing with unwanted sexual advances). It has a strong emphasis on consent – both saying 'no' and understanding when someone else says 'no', and throughout promotes safer sex and condom use. There are also topics on practical issues, such as where to get condoms and who to ask for advice.

The video uses a central character – Jason – who tells us about episodes in his life, from learning about his own body to forming a relationship with a young woman, Kylie (who is the subject of a similar resource – *Kylie's private world* – aimed at women with learning disabilities). Jason also narrates us through scenes showing someone successfully refusing unwanted sexual advances. The video emphasises that it is your choice who you form sexual relationships with. Reference is made to same-sex relationships, but these are not explored in depth.

The video is in sections, each of which covers a separate topic. The pack takes you chronologically through these sections, using images from the video, giving a summary of what is said, and containing guidance for facilitators on issues that may arise. For example, in the section on consent it advises support workers to be prepared for individual viewers bringing up situations they themselves have been in, suggesting they should be ready to provide counselling and to involve other agencies if needed. The notes also suggest follow-on activities for each topic – for example bringing in photos of yourselves as children when looking at the changes from childhood to adulthood, or practising using condoms on courgettes.

Photocopiable diagrams of Jason's and Kylie's bodies are provided to help viewers. These are clear and simple, although in Kylie's diagram there is no reference to the clitoris.

The pack advises that some sections of the video may cause embarrassment. Because it uses animation the video is able to be explicit about intercourse, sexual positions, and masturbation. It is suggested that the video is used with individuals or in single sex groups. It would benefit from viewing in short sections, topic by topic, with time for discussion and questions to ensure information has been absorbed and understood.

The notes also include a list of relevant contacts and resources for people with learning disabilities and support workers. Most of the resources listed were produced before 1991, and it therefore does not include the many useful resources produced on sex education in the past five years.

Keep yourself healthy – a guide to examining your testicles

FORMAT: Booklet, 14-pages
AUDIENCE: Men with learning disabilities
PRICE: free (first copy); £1.00 (subsequent copies)
PRODUCER: Edinburgh: Family Advice and Information Resource, 1998
DISTRIBUTOR: Family Advice and Information Resource

This booklet contains information on testicular self-examination for men with learning disabilities. It explains why early detection of cancer is necessary.

Through the use of cartoons and simple text, the booklet describes how to check testicles. For example, it explains that this should be done in the warm and in private. Diagrams show how to carry out an examination and the signs to look for that may indicate problems. The booklet gives advice about seeking help and concludes with some basic tips on staying healthy. Men are advised to talk to a key worker or community nurse if they have any questions.

The information is simply presented and requires basic reading skills if it is to be used by an individual on his own. However, it could be used by healthcare professionals, residential staff, and key workers as a teaching aid, possibly as part of a wider programme on cancer or sex education. Facilitators using this booklet would need to have a broader understanding of sex and relationship issues for men and to feel confident about raising sensitive issues.

The cartoons all feature white men and the text is primarily 14 point, which would make the booklet accessible to some partially sighted men with learning disabilities.

Keeping house

FORMAT: Pack – ring-bound resource file; 72 routine cards; routine card display wallet; pocket book; 55 photocopy originals; 2 display pages; instructor's guide
AUDIENCE: Young people and adults with learning disabilities
PRICE: £99.95 + VAT
PRODUCER: USA: Attainment Company Inc.
DISTRIBUTOR: Winslow Press

This pack, produced in the USA, is a comprehensive guide on how to carry out household tasks. The topics covered include: general skills; bathroom; bedroom; kitchen; laundry; indoor maintenance (such as changing light bulbs or feeding pets) and outdoor maintenance (such as mowing grass or raking leaves). The resource can be used with individuals or groups of up to four people, and should be used in conjunction with, but not necessarily in, their home. The pack is very detailed and would save a lot of time, particularly where material is needed for people who do not read. Access to a photocopier is essential for the participants and trainer to build up portfolios, pocket books, or displays either for each individual or for a household.

The pack comes in three parts. The first and main part consists of 48 'step pages'. An activity – for example, cleaning the bath – is broken down into steps, with notes on any specific points or problems to be aware of. An A4 card shows this sequence illustrated in black-and-white drawings. The cards can be used as step-by-step instructions when learning a new skill, or specific steps can be cut out and used as prompts, or the steps can be mixed up and people asked to arrange them in the correct order. The authors suggest adapting both written and picture steps to relate them more specifically to a given household. Some of the sequences may not be clear to some people with learning disabilities and may need to be broken down into more steps. The illustrations include people from black and minority ethnic groups but not disabled people. The cards are not laminated and may get worn with use.

The second part is a set of 72 colour laminated routine cards that each show an activity. These are each the size of a credit card. They can be used as memory prompts, as a way of promoting record-keeping by participants, and as a language resource. A box is provided to keep them in.

The third part is the programme plan. This includes assessment sheets to record a person's skills before, during, and after the programme. There are also goal sheets that set objectives for the learning of a particular activity or step within an activity. For example, the ability to fill the watering can in the 'Watering the house plants' activity. Finally, there are report sheets for homes and educational establishments to use to communicate with each other about the programme.

The resource includes comprehensive notes for facilitators about planning and leading the programme. It could be used with adults learning to live more independently, with young people preparing to leave home, or with people learning to take on more responsibility in a household.

Keeping my home safe from fire: a training video for use with people with learning disabilities

FORMAT: Video pack – video 30 mins; notes, 12-pages; leaflets x 2 – 'Wake up! Get a smoke alarm' and 'A fire survival guide'
AUDIENCE: People with learning disabilities
AUTHORS: North and West Belfast Health and Social Services Trust, and Northern Ireland Fire Brigade
PRICE: £58.69 + p&p
PRODUCER: Belfast: North and West Belfast Health and Social Services Trust, 1996
DISTRIBUTOR: Pavilion Publishing Ltd

This is a video-based training pack about fire safety for people with learning disabilities who live alone or in shared accommodation in the community.

The fire safety routine was designed by North and West Belfast Health and Social Services Trust in conjunction with the Northern Ireland Fire Brigade. There are accompanying leaflets from the Home Office. It offers a specific set of rules for people with learning disabilities to learn about fire safety in their own homes. The rules are practical and easy to understand. They are clearly laid out in three sections: Causes of fire; Smoke alarms and fire safety night time routine; and Your fire escape plan.

The resource is designed for support workers to use with individuals or small groups in their own homes. It consists of a video, group discussions, and practical exercises. The accompanying booklet for trainers includes helpful ideas and advice about how to make the routine accessible to people with a wide variety of intellectual abilities.

The video can be used as the main teaching element or to reinforce more practical tasks, depending upon the group. It uses male and female tenants with a learning disability as role models to demonstrate the fire routine. The messages are reinforced by verbal and written instructions and by repetition so the pack could be used in the context of facilitated groupwork with people with sight difficulties. The video can be used in one session or as a series, and each section of the video has space built in for discussion and for practical exercises.

Kylie's private world

FORMAT: Video pack – video 20 mins; notes, 26-pages, illustrated
AUDIENCE: Girls and young women with learning disabilities
PRICE: £50.00 + VAT
PRODUCER: London: Life Support Productions, 1996
DISTRIBUTOR: Life Support Productions
This animated video is intended for use by young women and girls with learning disabilities as part of a general sex education programme. It was developed in response to feedback on an earlier sex education video, *You, your body and sex*. It is accompanied by viewing notes and a resource list.
The pack covers 17 different topics ranging from the physical aspects of sex education (such as body changes from childhood to adulthood, menstruation, breast self-examination, and personal hygiene) to emotional and social dimensions (such as relationships, love, affection, consent, being alone, and dealing with unwanted sexual advances). It has a strong focus on consent – both saying 'no' and understanding when someone else says 'no' – and throughout promotes safer sex and condom use. Emphasis is put on getting to know what is normal for your body and becoming aware of abnormal changes – for example, in the sections on menstruation and breast examination, which offer clear visual and verbal information on these two topics. There are also topics on practical issues, such as where to get condoms and who to ask for advice.
The video uses a central character, Kylie, who tells us about episodes in her life, from learning about her own body to forming a relationship with a young man, Jason (who is the subject of a similar resource – *Jason's private world* – aimed at men with learning disabilities). Kylie also narrates us through scenes showing a woman successfully saying 'no' to unwanted sexual advances on a train. The video emphasises that it is your choice who you form sexual relationships with. Reference is made to same-sex relationships, although these are not explored in depth.
The video is in sections, each of which covers a separate topic. The pack takes you chronologically through these sections, using images from the video, giving a summary of what is said, and containing guidance for facilitators on issues that may arise. For example, in the section on consent it advises support workers to be prepared for individual viewers bringing up situations they themselves have been in, suggesting supporters should be ready to provide counselling and to involve other agencies if needed. The notes also suggest follow-on activities for each topic – for example, bringing in photos of yourselves as children when looking at the changes from childhood to adulthood, or practising using condoms on courgettes.
Photocopiable diagrams of Kylie's and Jason's bodies are provided to help viewers. These are clear and simple; in Kylie's diagram there is no reference to the clitoris, though this is mentioned in the section on masturbation in the video.

Because it uses animation, the video is able to be explicit about intercourse, sexual positions, and masturbation. The pack advises that some sections of the video may cause embarrassment. It is suggested that the video is used with individuals or in single sex groups. It would benefit from viewing in short sections, topic by topic, with time for discussion and questions to ensure information has been absorbed and understood.

The notes also include a list of relevant contacts and resources for people with learning disabilities and support workers. Most of the resources listed were produced before 1991, and it therefore does not include the many useful resources produced on sex education in the past five years.

Learning disability: working as equal people

FORMAT: Multimedia – guide, 60-pages, illustrated; workbooks (x3), 99-pages, 109-pages, 106-pages; videos (x2), 30 mins each; audio cassettes (x4); booklet, 53-pages; Guides to Open College Network and Pathways to NVQs

AUDIENCE: People with learning disabilities

PRICE: £86.00 inc.; £74.43 + VAT (study pack only); £17.00 inc. (assessment pack only)

PRODUCER: Milton Keynes: School of Health and Social Welfare, The Open University, 1996

DISTRIBUTOR: LMSO, Open University

ISBN: 0749245301 (set)

Working as equal people is an Open University distance learning pack. The course is intended for people with learning disabilities, staff, and carers. It aims to enable them to work together to plan and change things that affect them.

A guide, *Using equal people*, prepares participants for the course, looks at ways of studying, either by yourself, with a study partner, or in a group, and gives advice to group leaders and supporters about group meetings. There is an audio cassette with the guide in which parents, carers, and people with learning disabilities who piloted the course speak about their experiences as students. There are sections on: working with study partners and supporters; the role of facilitators; learning in groups; the difficulties of the course; and the benefits of building partnerships between staff, parents, and people with learning disabilities to bring about personal and wider social change.

The main course materials are three workbooks. Workbook 1, *Finding out about the past and present*, asks participants to look at their own life and the lives of others as they are now and as they used to be. This includes you, whether you are a person with a learning disability, a parent, or a member of staff. Workbook 2, *Speaking out for equal rights*, involves people with learning disabilities, carers, and staff in finding out about rights and responsibilities. Workbook 3, *Working together for change*, looks at different ways of working together as partners, as supporters, as advocates, or in groups. It asks participants to think about the best ways of working for change in their situation. Each workbook has its own accompanying audio cassette. The books and cassettes are colour coded.

The workbooks are activity based and each covers 10 topics. Some activities enable people to build up a portfolio about themselves and their situation; a separate booklet looks at why building a portfolio is important and how it could be used, for example, to value your own experience, apply for a job, or identify your skills. Other activities help participants listen to and watch the tapes actively. All the activities require the participants to do something and to record it.

There are a number of other videos and cassettes to be studied at different points in the course, including *The shampoo set* (a video drama); *Looking at people's lives* (five short documentaries); and *It's not the same* (a drama serial on cassette). The pack includes a comprehensive Resource Book giving details of other books, videos, packs, and organisations that might help students follow up ideas. These are indexed by topic.

The course shows people with learning disabilities as equal people, and carers as people with needs, wants, and lives outside their family. It will increase participants' knowledge about services and policies, and enable them to work together more effectively and to learn about each other. Throughout the materials, the main voices are those of people with learning disabilities. The materials themselves use simple language, photos and drawings, video and audio-tape, which makes them adaptable according to the needs and communication skills of different groups or individuals. There is a 'short route' through the course using only the most accessible materials. The course can be linked to qualifications, such as the Open College Network credits or NVQs and details are given in the pathways guide.

Learning to love: a set of simple booklets on sex

FORMAT: Booklets (x5), 24-pages, illustrated
AUDIENCE: People with learning disabilities
AUTHOR: Fraser, J.
PRICE: £15.00 inc. (for set of 5 booklets)
PRODUCER: London: Brook Advisory Centres, 1991 and 1997 (revised)
DISTRIBUTOR: Brook Advisory Centres

This is a series of five illustrated sexual health booklets produced in 1991. One of the series, *Sex, health and infections*, was revised in 1997. They include illustrations on almost every page – black-and-white line drawings with some grey shading. They are clear whole body drawings, mostly of young black and white people with no distracting background. Men are shown in caring roles, such as holding the baby or attending a clinic with their partner. Some of the pictures are sexually explicit. The text is in large print with important words in bold type making it accessible to some people with partial sight. Sentences are short with a simple vocabulary, but help may be needed with terms that may be unfamiliar, such as 'placenta' or 'ovum'. Some of the booklets contain more text than others, as some information can be illustrated more easily – for example, the male and female anatomy.

The booklets in the series are:

- *From child to adult: growing up, puberty, adolescence.* This booklet gives information on the physical and emotional changes of puberty for men and women, menstruation, and male and female masturbation.
- *Sex: making love, having sex.* This booklet gives information on men's and women's bodies, sexual arousal in men and women, and heterosexual intercourse, including foreplay.
- *Sex, health and infections.* This booklet, revised in 1997, gives information on different kinds of infections, parts of the body that may be affected, what is 'healthy' and not 'healthy' for women and men, basic hygiene, how to get help, what happens at a special clinic, and using condoms for safer sex.
- *Contraception: birth control, family planning.* This booklet gives

information on why contraception is needed, men's and women's bodies, sexual intercourse, contraceptive methods (including 'morning after' or emergency contraception), using a condom for safer sex, and where to get help with contraception.
- *How a baby starts and how a baby is born.* This booklet gives information on (planned) conception, pregnancy, the growth of the baby, and birth.

Information is presented in a straightforward way and would be useful as part of a sex education programme. The booklets can be used privately by those who have reading skills, but they would be enhanced by help from a facilitator to ensure information is understood and to enable discussion of feelings about growing up, as well as facts.

Let's be clear

FORMAT: Video, 30 mins
AUDIENCE: Adults with learning disabilities, support workers, social workers, healthcare professionals
PRICE: £50.00 + VAT
PRODUCER: Bristol: Home Farm Trust, 1998
DISTRIBUTOR: Home Farm Trust Trading

This training video is aimed at support workers, social workers and other healthcare professionals working with adults with learning disabilities. As an introduction to communication it would be accessible to people with little or no experience of learning disabilities. It might also help some learning disabled people to identify and talk about communication difficulties in general.

The aim of this resource is to raise awareness about the common misunderstandings that occur in our verbal and non-verbal communications with learning disabled people. The popular actor Griff Rhys Jones introduces the video and two learning-disabled people talk about the difficulties they experience. This is followed by four stories entitled 'Miles apart', 'Causing confusion', 'The right time and the right place', and 'Getting it right'.

Actors, including learning disabled men and women, appear in these scenarios, which take place in residential, day activity and work experience settings. The first three stories clearly illustrate the mistakes that are frequently made. After each one Griff Rhys Jones identifies the problems, suggests ways of improving skills, and highlights the positive benefits for all concerned. 'Getting it right' presents a positive illustration of clear, effective communication.

A summary at the end of the video highlights the importance of: knowing your client's level of understanding; making sure you give your full attention; making use of context and situation; tone of voice and gestures; the use of simple words and short sentences, speaking slowly; the use of objects, symbols, and signs; and the importance of showing how you value what is being said.

There is no reference to cultural differences, although one learning disabled actor is from a minority ethnic group. The video works well as an audio-only resource because of the clear narration and introduction of characters and settings, which makes it more accessible for blind and partially sighted people.

This video is suitable for either formal or informal settings and can be viewed by individuals or in groups. It was produced by the Home Farm Trust in collaboration with The Nora Fry Research Centre with the support of the Paul Spain Group.

Let's do it: creative activities for sex education for young people with learning disabilities

FORMAT: Pack, 168-pages
AUDIENCE: People with learning disabilities, teachers, support workers, youth workers
AUTHOR: Johns, R. Scott, L. and Bliss, J.
PRICE: £14.00 plus £2.50 p&p
PRODUCER: Somerset: Image in Action, 1997
DISTRIBUTOR: Image in Action
This pack is a compendium of activities for those who teach sex education to people with learning disabilities in schools, colleges, and adult centres, group homes. Many of the activities are aimed at students with severe learning disabilities but can be adapted to suit a wide range of needs and abilities.
The pack follows on from the previous Image in Action publication entitled On the Agenda (1994) which was a three-part guide to teaching sex education. Let's Do It is divided into eight themes or sections, preceded by an introduction that looks at planning and running sessions. The themes are: Group building; Body parts; Gender; Public and private; Feelings; Relationships (including HIV/AIDS); Life cycle; and Skills.
The pack is flexible and could be used to plan courses and select activities, depending upon the length of time available. Guidelines for use include a curriculum framework for sex education and sample session plans. Each activity is clearly set out. Since all the activities are drama-based or use visual images, there are no written handouts or other materials. There is a review of basic drama and active learning methods.
On equality issues, the producer acknowledges the right to information of people with learning disabilities regardless of gender, age, sexual orientation, disability, race, or religion. The pack was developed in conjunction with several schools, colleges and day centres in various London boroughs, and was supported by BBC Children in Need, the Sir John Cass Foundation, and Ealing Mencap.

Living safely: at home and on the bus

FORMAT: Video, 15 mins
AUDIENCE: People with learning disabilities
PRICE: £25.00 (advocacy groups); £28.00 (other groups)
PRODUCER: Rotherham: Speakup Self Advocacy, Mencap (Rotherham) Streetwise Project, 1996
DISTRIBUTOR: Speakup Self Advocacy
This video is one of a series produced by Speakup, a self-advocacy group in Rotherham. Other titles in the series include *How to go into hospital, What can I do if I'm arrested*?, and *How can I make a complaint*? All of the videos are devised by people with learning disabilities and aim to make information more accessible.
Living safely looks at safety skills and focuses in detail on two situations: dealing with callers to your home; and travelling by bus. Each section of the video is identified with a title and voice-over, and consists of a number of dramatised scenes, acted by people with and without learning disabilities. All the actors are white but of various ages.
Each of the short drama scenes shows a sequence of events in which the main character does not act safely (a red cross is on screen for the duration of the scene); the scene is then repeated showing safer ways of dealing with the same situation (with a green tick permanently on screen). The device of using a red cross or a green tick to indicate unsafe and safe behaviour is explained clearly at the start of the

programme and helps to ensure that the 'unsafe' scenes are not taken as a model. The scenes are clear and concise; a voice over by a person with a learning disability sets up the scene and identifies the key points at the end. For example, in the section on offers of help, a man knocks at a couple's door and persuades them to let him repair their roof. They tell him they have money in the bank. After waiting outside reading the paper he returns, says he's done the repairs and charges them £400. The scene ends with him accompanying them to the bank. A voice-over asks 'What did Lewis and Shirley do that wasn't safe?' and then gives a list: they didn't use their door chain so they couldn't decide not to let the builder in; they believed what he said about the faulty roof without checking it; they agreed to his price and told him about their bank account without checking with someone they trusted. The scene is then repeated with Lewis and Shirley using the door chain: the builder is unable to come in and they tell him they will check on the roof themselves.

The video includes two other situations showing how to deal safely with callers, first someone unknown who wants to come into your home and then door-to-door sellers, and one situation showing a bus journey in which a man starts sexually harassing a woman. The scenes are realistic and relevant to people with learning disabilities living in the community. Some of them have a comic edge – for example, at the end of the scene about door-to-door sellers, the central character tells us 'I bought dog food and I haven't even got a dog'.

Although no clear pause points are indicated on screen, the 'unsafe' scenes can be used to trigger discussion about the safety issues they raise. They would also be a useful stimulus for work exploring wider safety issues, for example what information should be kept private, or to develop assertiveness skills. The video would be useful in work with either groups or individuals.

Living with difficult epilepsy

FORMAT: Video pack – video 25 mins; A4 notes,
15-pages
AUDIENCE: Parents of children with epilepsy
PRICE: £14.50 inc. (sale); £5.00 inc. (hire)
PRODUCER: Leeds: British Epilepsy Association, 1994
DISTRIBUTOR: British Epilepsy Association

This video was produced by the British Epilepsy Association with a grant from CIBA Pharmaceuticals. A presenter in a TV studio interviews several white families with children of various ages about their experiences of 'difficult' epilepsy. 'Difficult' epilepsy refers to epilepsy which is difficult to control and results in frequent fits. Questions are mainly directed to the parents and start with descriptions of the frequency and type of epilepsy from which their child suffers. A doctor talks about different types of epilepsy and medical procedures for identifying the causes and treatment of epilepsy. A headmaster talks about epilepsy within his school and stresses the importance of the child receiving appropriate education. Families describe their experiences of mainstream and special schools.

Some of the children featured in the video have learning disabilities and one young woman talks of taking her A levels in a mainstream school. The final section shows how families adapt their homes and lifestyles to ensure the safety of their child.

This video is primarily aimed at the parents of children with epilepsy and comes with 15 A4 pages of typed information about epilepsy, medication, and descriptions of different syndromes. Parts of the video could be used to trigger discussion about living with epilepsy with individuals or small groups of adults with moderate learning disabilities who are affected by epilepsy.

Making friends

FORMAT: Book, 68-pages, illustrated
AUDIENCE: Young people and adults with learning disabilities
AUTHORS: Hollins, S., Roth, T. and Webb, B. (illustrator)
PRICE: £10.00
PRODUCER: St George's Hospital Mental Health Library, 1995
DISTRIBUTOR: (Book Sales), Royal College of Psychiatrists
ISBN: 1 874439 10 9

This colour picture book was written by a psychiatrist and a clinical psychologist and is part of the *Books beyond words* series for people with learning disabilities.

The 33 illustrations tell a story about appropriate touching from a man's perspective. *Hug me, touch me* (p.81) tells a similar story from a woman's perspective. The pictures are clear and expressive and readers are encouraged to tell the story in their own words. There is a blank page between each of the pictures where people can draw their own pictures or add their own words if they wish. Words for each page are included at the end of the book for those who prefer a ready-made story. The story follows Neil, a young man who goes for a walk in a park. In an attempt to be friendly, he tries to hug a woman who is sitting reading a book, to play with some children, and to hug a pair of lovers. In each case, he is rejected by these people who are all strangers. Hurt and upset, Neil goes home and telephones a friend. The friend comes round, listens, hugs, and comforts him. The two friends then go out together, and meet people they know. They all greet each other appropriately and Neil goes home happy and reflects upon what he has learned about touching. The characters vary in age; the main character and his friend are white; their friends are black.

The book could be used by someone alone who has limited reading skills or be read with someone. The pictures are very powerful and facial expressions and colour vividly convey feelings. It could be used by both adults and children as the visual imagery is so clear – there are no distracting details, just strong colour and expressive body language. It could be used with groups or individuals to explore appropriate greeting and touch between people and would fit well in a programme of social skills education.

Making links: a video exploring mental health issues in people with learning disabilities

FORMAT: Video, 35 mins; leaflet
AUDIENCE: Parents, families, support workers, healthcare professionals
PRICE: £65.00 + VAT
PRODUCER: London: First Field, 1997
DISTRIBUTOR: Pavilion Publishing Ltd.

This video was made for anyone who supports people with a learning disability in the community and who may not have much knowledge or experience of mental health problems. This could be family members, support workers, nurses, or others who play a key role in detecting the first signs of a mental health problem, enabling an individual to access services, and be part of a co-ordinated intervention. *Making links* aims to raise awareness of the particular needs of people with learning disabilities. It sets out to inform the viewer about the signs and symptoms that might indicate whether a mental health problem exists. Identifying this is often complicated by the presence of a learning disability.

Three fictional stories about learning disabled people who develop a mental health problem are sensitively discussed by a panel of support staff and mental health professionals. A variety of physical, emotional, and behavioural symptoms are identified and possible causes explored. A variety of ways are then suggested in which each person might be supported in a co-ordinated intervention.

The accompanying leaflet suggests various ways in which this resource might be used and includes a number of useful questions for the viewer(s) to consider. It is complemented by the training package called *Mental health in learning disabilities,* which expands on the issues raised in this innovative video. It can be viewed by individuals or groups, in formal or informal settings. Characters portrayed in the stories include people from black and minority ethnic groups.

This project was supported by Lewisham and Guy's Mental Health NHS Trust, The Division of Psychiatry and Psychology, UMDS, and the Guy's Hospital Special Trustees.

Mary complains: a video and resource pack about making complaints for people with learning disabilities

FORMAT: Pack – video, 25 mins; notes, 45-pages, illustrated
AUDIENCE: People with learning disabilities, service providers
AUTHORS: Slater, D. and Hughes, A.
PRICE: £70.44 inc. + p&p; £46.94 inc. + p&p for self-advocacy groups
PRODUCER: Brighton: Pavilion Publishing, 1995
DISTRIBUTOR: Pavilion Publishing Ltd
ISBN: 1871080525

Mary complains is a video and resource pack about making complaints, aimed both at people with learning disabilities and service providers. It is intended to help services ensure that their complaints procedures are accessible and practical, and to empower service users to express their concerns. It should be used in conjunction with specific complaints procedures.

The video shows a series of drama scenes, focusing on Mary, an elderly woman with a learning disability. Mary becomes angry when a set she has been working on for her drama group is thrown away by a member of staff. A friend helps her to make a complaint. The scenes work as a continuous story, but the video is best shown in sections, each lasting a couple of minutes. Each section raises a different set of issues relating to complaints: the way people with learning disabilities are treated by staff; the choices people have at home; problems with people you live with; privacy; and the process of making a complaint itself. The scenes are realistic, improvised by actors with and without learning disabilities. All the main performers in the video are white.

The pack divides into four main sections. Section 1 provides an overview of different methods of organising complaints procedures and contains suggestions and a checklist for developing good practice. Section 2 describes how to work with the video. It provides notes on each of the six episodes, which include a summary of the story, discussion points, action points, and supplementary notes for support workers. Section 3 explains role-play techniques and how they can be used to enable people with learning disabilities to explore the issues addressed in the pack. It provides five different scenarios which could be used as starting points for role-play work. Section 4 contains guidelines intended for staff who know someone who has something to complain about.

The resource would be useful for training staff and supporters, but is particularly appropriate for work with people with learning disabilities on a specific complaints procedure, or to encourage a climate where complaints are welcomed and acted upon. It could be used in groups or with an individual who wants to make a complaint, watching with a supporter.

Meaningful lives

FORMAT: Video, 35 mins
AUDIENCE: People with learning dsiabilities
PRICE: £11.50 inc.
PRODUCER: Bridgend and Persondy Day Centres, 1995
DISTRIBUTOR: Valley and Vale Community Arts Ltd.

This video was devised and produced by a group of adults with learning disabilities from two day centres in Mid Glamorgan, with the help of Valley and Vale, a community arts team. It was funded by Mid Glamorgan Social Services Department. The video consists predominantly of interviews with the group who speak about their lives and touch on a wide range of issues such as discrimination, bullying, relationships, parenthood, marriage, and sports. There is a mix of positive images and some honest discussion of the limitations facing people with learning disabilities. The people interviewed demonstrate a breadth of awareness and experience in their discussions. It is targeted at people with a learning disability.

The video can be viewed as a whole or in sections. It is divided into four parts: Likes and dislikes; Opportunities and obstacles; Rights and responsibilities; and Hopes and fears. The video is introduced by one of the group who says 'We can do things that other people may not think we can do. We're going to show you.'

In each section, members of the group speak to camera; occasionally they visit places that are connected with their ambitions – for example, a rugby stadium, a theatre and a lifeguard station. Family relationships are a recurring theme. For example, in Opportunities and obstacles, one of the group, Julie, speaks about her new flat where she lives independently. Another of the group says she would like her own flat, but is stopped from moving because she thinks she should stay and look after her mother. A third group member says he worries about what may happen in the future when his mother dies. Two of the group speak about their relationship – how they met at 16, were parted for some years, then met up again when they went to the same day centre. They say there's a wall between what they want (to live together and have children) and their actual lives, because of people's attitudes to their relationship, and particularly the attitudes of their families. Many of the issues in the video are about other people's reactions to learning disability. One of the group speaks about being bullied on the bus; another member of the group suggests he should stand up for himself and make people aware how it affects him. One woman says she feels she would be capable of going on holiday on her own, but wouldn't be allowed to without day centre staff. The group includes people from a wide age range, but all are white.

The video also touches on money, benefits, leisure, shopping, and the group's views on world events. Occasionally it mixes in news footage of Bosnia, the Berlin Wall, and urban riots. It is intended 'as a starting point for discussion' and could be used with groups or individuals to explore self-advocacy issues, particularly in relation to families. It would be a helpful tool to introduce new health and social care students and workers to the lives of people with disabilities. There is no accompanying material.

Michelle finds a voice

FORMAT: Book, 80-pages, illustrated
AUDIENCE: People with severe communication impairment, carers, support workers
PRICE: £10.00 inc.
PRODUCER: London: Gaskell and St George's Hospital Medical School, 1997
DISTRIBUTOR: Royal College of Psychiatrists, Book Sales
ISBN: 1901242064

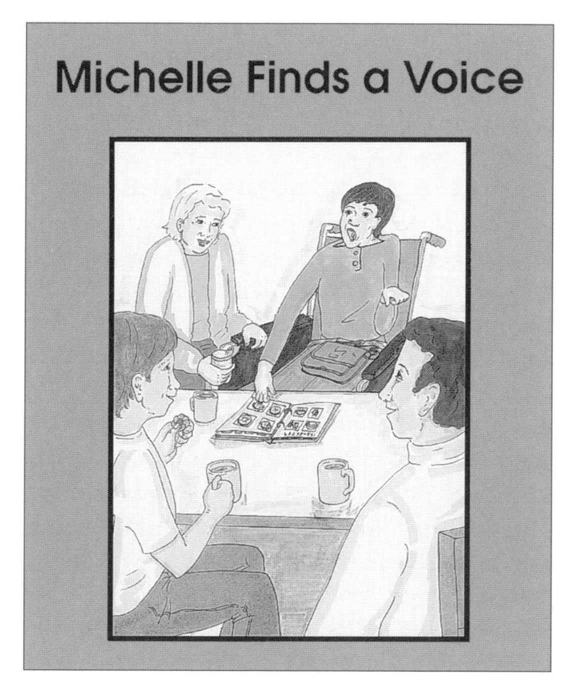

This colour picture book was written for people with a severe communication impairment, their carers, and others involved in their lives. It is one of the *Books beyond words* series.

It consists of 33 coloured illustrations that tell the story of a young, white woman, called Michelle, who has cerebral palsy. Because Michelle cannot speak she is unable to communicate her thoughts and feelings to others and becomes frustrated and depressed. This is graphically depicted in a variety of situations, such as going to the hairdressers, feeling left out in social situations, and experiencing a traumatic robbery. Some of the other characters involved come from black and minority ethic groups.

Michelle's distress is recognised by her carer, and the reader learns how Michelle is then helped to explore the use of alternative ways of expressing herself at a Communications Aids Centre. There is a happy ending in which Michelle is seen communicating with others, making choices, and developing social relationships.

This story can be accompanied by the given text or, as the authors suggest, readers may wish to interpret the pictures for themselves. This resource may be unsuitable for some people with partial sight, for others enlargement may be necessary. There is also a useful section about communication at the back of the book. It describes augmentative and alternative systems and lists resource centres and communications organisations.

This book was written by a professor of psychiatry and a research speech and language therapist, both of whom have worked extensively with people with cerebral palsy and/or severe communication impairment. It was published jointly by the Royal College of Psychiatrists and St George's Hospital Medical School, and was financially supported by Communication Matters.

Movement activities for children with learning difficulties

FORMAT: Book, 112-pages
AUDIENCE: Teachers of children with special needs
AUTHOR: Pointer, B.
price: £12.99 + 10% p&p
PRODUCER: London: Jessica Kingsley Publishers, 1993
DISTRIBUTOR: Jessica Kingsley Publishers
ISBN: 1 85302 167 9

This book is a resource for teachers. It contains over 120 physical activities for children with mild learning disabilities. This includes children who may suffer from hyperactivity, impulsivity, movement problems, or disorders of memory, perception, attention, or language. The book is aimed at teachers in mainstream schools who have children with special needs in their classes. The activities listed are mostly mainstream physical education activities.

The introduction contains a short description of the developmental motor stages of children, and the need to assess whether children have missed a stage and therefore need to learn its associated skills. It stresses the need to be aware of a child's learning disability and to adapt the activities to that individual. However, the games listed make no mention of how to adapt them for people with particular physical impairments – for example, wheelchair users or children with hearing difficulties.

The activities are divided into four sections: warm-up activities for groups; pair work; small group work; and large group work. Each activity is described with notes on its value and variant versions. For example, certain games may be good for the development of peripheral vision, hand–eye co-ordination, spatial awareness, or co-operation. These brief descriptions are useful.

The book does not include case studies or suggestions for teaching children with particular problems. There are a few black-and-white photographs of children doing some of the activities. The activities are well indexed and there is a bibliography of other useful books.

Moving on: access of services by people with learning difficulties

FORMAT: Video pack – video 27 mins; booklet, 27-pages
AUDIENCE: People with learning disabilities
AUTHOR: Lambeth Social Services and Lambeth, Southwark, and Lewisham Health Authority
PRICE: £50.00 + VAT
PRODUCER: London: Magpie Productions, 1997
DISTRIBUTOR: Magpie Productions

This video was designed for people with a learning disability to help them understand something of health and social services provision, particularly the process of assessment and care planning. The central message is that service providers are there to help people take control of their own lives and to support them in their growing independence. The video was made by Lambeth Social Services Department in partnership with Lambeth, Southwark, and Lewisham Health Authority.

The video tells the story of a young black woman struggling to persuade her family that she wants to live independently and being helped towards her goal by social services. The narrative is broken down into 11 parts that can be viewed separately. They incorporate the following: Problems at home; Getting started – referral; Family

assessment; Private assessment; Care plan; Community support; Education; Shopping; Speaking out; Housing; and Review.
The young woman is encouraged to work towards her goal by using the resources available – doing a college foundation course, joining a self-advocacy group, having a community support worker, and meeting people already living independently. Her programme is put together with care and sensitivity and the video ends with her ready to move and waiting for a flat to become available.
The video demonstrates the wide range of facilities available to people wanting to move on and offers education and encouragement. It will be useful to self-advocacy groups and care staff wanting to explore the issue of independent living. It will also encourage those who want to live independently but are nervous. The video presents a valuable model of good practice for students and staff working in assessment and care planning and will be good training material for any agency involved with people facing this experience, particularly general practitioners, community nurses, and carers.
The video is made by disabled actors representing different black and minority ethnic groups. It is structured to be a useful narrative for people with partial sight.

My cook book

FORMAT: Book A4, 141-pages, illustrated
AUDIENCE: People with learning disabilities
PRICE: £19.95 + 5% p&p
AUTHOR: Marshall, R.M.
PRODUCER: Kidderminster: British Institute of Learning Disabilities (BILD), 1993
DISTRIBUTOR: BILD Publications, Plymbridge Distributors
ISBN: £1 873791 10 0

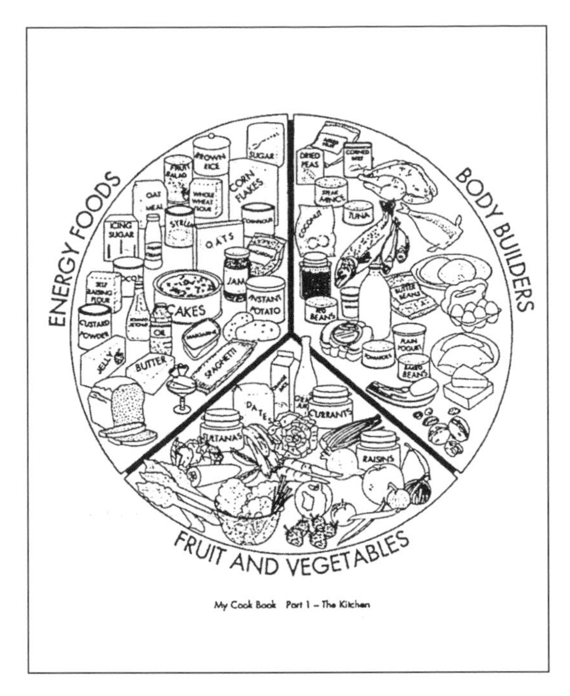

My Cook Book Part 1 – The Kitchen

A cookbook for people who may have problems following instructions or who have reading difficulties. *My cook book* can be used as a teaching resource or a cookbook for those living independently. The book brings together several aspects of kitchen life, not just cooking. Each topic or recipe is illustrated with clear black-and-white line drawings. Each recipe has a page to itself and the book can be folded over so that only the recipe is visible, thus reducing visual distractions.
Topics covered in the introduction include hygiene for self and food, washing-up techniques, and safety issues including the dangers involved in boiling, frying, steaming, and baking. Also included is a pictorial glossary of basic equipment, clear diagrams on units of measurement, heat, and how best to store food. The nutritional value of types of food and the idea of a mixed diet are clearly presented with worksheets. Microwave cookery is not included.
Recipes are colour coded and fall into simple (62) and more complex (50) types. Ingredients and utensils needed are clearly drawn at the top of each page, and each

step in the preparation sequence is drawn and described in a few words. The final section includes some planned menus and how to make a variety of packed lunches. People without reading skills may be able to use the book but will need some preparation on how to 'read' the pictures, which are about an inch and a half square. Some colour coding should be added, for instance to indicate the degree of heat used in each recipe. The use of acetate overlays so people can tick off items may also help.

The book is comprehensive in its coverage, easy to use, and should encourage the development of cooking skills.

My life, my story: making personal portfolios

FORMAT: Video, 20 mins
AUDIENCE: People with learning disabilities
PRICE: £40.00 + VAT
PRODUCER: Manchester: Manchester People First, 1998
DISTRIBUTOR: Manchester People First

Seven members of the Manchester People First Group made this video. They set out to show other people with learning disabilities and their supporters that everyone has an important story to tell about their own unique life.

Some of the people taking part have profound and multiple impairments. This gives a positive and encouraging message to others with severe disabilities and those that help them. Members of the group include both young and older people, as well as one woman from a minority ethnic group.

'This is your life – it's up to you' says Donovan, the presenter. He takes the viewer(s) through several steps to help them think about making a personal portfolio and demonstrates with other people in the film that there are many ways of doing it. Some people communicate through touch and smell or using objects they may feel especially connected to. Other people choose to make an audio or visual record of their lives. Fariana, a young Muslim woman, finds a sense of identity by handling some of the artefacts of her religion and culture. For each person in this group, the pleasure in the whole process of creating and using their portfolio is abundantly evident. Perhaps it is this that conveys one of the most powerful messages in this video, that 'Your life is important and your story is worth recording.' Project workers, supporters, and volunteers speak enthusiastically about the positive effects this has had on the people they have helped.

For people with sight difficulties the large script, uncomplicated dialogue, and accompanying music combine to convey clear messages and information.

This video was funded by the Jospeh Rowntree Foundation's 'People, plans and possibilities' project.

A new home in the community

FORMAT: Book, 72-pages, illustrated
AUDIENCE: People with learning disabilities
AUTHORS: Hollins, S., Hutchinson, D. and Webb, B. (illustrator)
PRICE: £10.00 inc.
PUBLISHER: London: St George's Mental Health Library, 1993
DISTRIBUTOR: Royal College of Psychiatrists, Book Sales
ISBN: 1 874439 02 8

This colour picture book was written by two consultant psychiatrists and is part of the *Books beyond words* series for people with learning disabilities. It is intended for use with people who are making the transition from living in a long stay hospital or hostel to living in a group home. The book contains colour illustrations facing a page of simple text, beginning and ending with the characters looking at photographs of the places they have lived.

The book tells the story of Simon, who leaves his home, carers, and friends when he moves from hospital to a group home. The illustrations show Simon worrying about leaving, but making the decision to move, taking with him a favourite chair and giving leaving presents to his friends. It shows some of the problems he has settling in, for example missing his friends; when Simon returns to the hospital for a visit he becomes sad when it is time to say goodbye. Also included are scenes showing some of the things he enjoys in his new home, such as going out with new friends. The characters include people with physical disabilities and people from different ethnic groups.

This book is suitable for use with individuals with learning disabilities who are preparing to move to a smaller home in the community, to enable them to reflect on their feelings about the move and their new life.

A nightmare ... that I thought would never end

FORMAT: Pack – cassette; notes, 40-pages
AUDIENCE: People with learning disabilities who have been abused, support workers
AUTHOR: Stein, J. and Brown, H.
PRICE: £30.49 inc + p&p
PRODUCER: Brighton: Pavilion Publishing, 1996
DISTRIBUTOR: Pavilion Publishing Ltd

This audiotape was made with the involvement of a group of people with learning disabilities who are survivors of sexual abuse. The tape combines interviews with service users about their experiences, with additional comments and suggestions about how staff can prevent and respond to sexual abuse. The tape is intended for staff members and the booklet suggests it could be used in a range of settings: for example by individual members of staff before a planned supervision session, as part of an awareness training course, in work by joint care planning teams on service development or in sections as part of a longer course. The resource is intended to be used to help people to develop their awareness and skills, rather than as a response to a particular incident.

The tape is divided into four sections in which survivors speak movingly and graphically about their experiences. Section 1, Defining sexual abuse, explores the issues of power and consent which are key to any definition of sexual abuse. Survivors speak about their relationship to people who abused them – for example, close family members, relations, and day centre staff. They describe the kinds of abuse they faced and their feelings of powerlessness. Section 2 describes how survivors tried, and often failed, to tell someone about the abuse. It also looks at the unclear signals of distress a person may be giving and makes suggestions about how staff can respond sensitively to disclosures of abuse. Section 3 describes ways of working with survivors to help them work through their experiences.

It includes a recording of a staff member working with a survivor using explicit pictures and encouraging him to draw as a way of expressing what happened. The drawings are included in the accompanying booklet. Section 4 looks at planning services with the long-term needs of survivors in mind. Survivors describe the ways services responded to their situation, often taking no responsibility for their safety or support. This section also touches on the need for key workers to find adequate supervision and support for themselves.

The booklet accompanying the tape includes guidance notes for facilitators on how to plan training using the tape, together with a transcript. It contains a comprehensive list of other training materials, further reading, and useful addresses.

This resource will be invaluable in training staff working with people with a learning disability. It requires preparation and would be best used as part of a structured training programme. Some listeners may find the accounts it contains distressing, and it should be used in a safe setting, with time to debrief listeners afterwards. The sound quality is occasionally poor, but hearing people tell their own stories makes it compelling, if disturbing, listening.

No means no

FORMAT: Video, 20 mins; A4 illustrated looseleaf sheets (x6)
AUDIENCE: Women with learning disabilities
PRICE: £46.94 + 10% p&p
PRODUCER: Walsall: Walsall Women's Group, 1994
DISTRIBUTOR: Pavilion Publishing Ltd

This video pack aims to enable women with learning disabilities to explore personal safety. The resource was devised, produced, and performed by women with learning disabilities who are members of a women's group.

The video is divided into short sections covering personal safety at home, at work, and in relationships. Short scenes acted by group members show incidents where personal safety is at stake. These are accompanied by information about services that can provide support to women, such as the sexual health clinic, Victim Support, training in assertion and self-defence, and the police domestic violence unit. Women from the group visit each of these services and interview staff, asking important questions about access and confidentiality.

The accompanying pack looks at issues that came up during workshops at a conference organised by the women's group in 1993. The pack carries a mixture of easy-to-read text, photographs from the conference, and fact sheets which address the main subjects of the video. These tackle difficult areas such as bullying, assertion, and relationships with friends, and could be used as a focus for group discussion. Some women with learning disabilities who reviewed the pack said they felt the photographs were not always clearly explained. The pack does not contain any guidelines for using the video. A wide range of ages is represented in the video. All the women in the group are white and neither video nor pack addresses issues specific to women from black and minority ethnic groups.

The information about services in the video and pack is an excellent resource for women living in the Walsall area, but is of little use as a source of contacts for women outside the Midlands. Group workers who want to use *No means no* as an information resource would need to research similar services in their own area or perhaps use the video as a stimulus for women to find out about their local services as a group. Because of this potential confusion the resource needs careful facilitation. However, the drama scenes and interviews with service workers provide clear examples for discussion of both personal safety and available support for women with learning disabilities.

Now it makes sense!

FORMAT: Video (x4), 15 mins; notes, 9-pages
AUDIENCE: People with learning disabilities, primary healthcare teams
PRICE: £200.00 + VAT (set of 4 videos); £50.00 + VAT (single videos)
PRODUCER: Bournemouth: Dorset Healthcare NHS Trust, 1996
DISTRIBUTOR: Viewpoint Project
There are four videos in this series. They were produced as part of a wider strategy in Dorset to provide accessible information about health care, focusing particularly on information that does not rely on language skills. The videos explore different healthcare situations to improve effective communication by and with people with learning disabilities. The videos, reviewed separately, include: *Let's test your ears*, *Let's test your eyes*, *Seeing the dentist*, and *Seeing the doctor*.
The videos are accompanied by a booklet for support workers and carers. This suggests how to use the videos effectively, with advice on the environment the video is shown in, when to use it (for example, before a healthcare appointment), the sorts of augmentative communication that the support worker could use with the video, and ways of reinforcing the information it contains. It starts from the belief that familiarisation with procedures reduces anxiety and so makes healthcare more effective. The booklet suggests sharing the videos with the relevant healthcare professionals and, if possible, encouraging them to use similar techniques to those shown in the video in order to match the person's real experience with the experience shown. A number of practical activities are included to use alongside the videos – for example, using objects of reference such as hearing aids, optical equipment, toothbrush, and stethoscope.

Now it makes sense: let's test your ears

FORMAT: Video, 15 mins; notes
AUDIENCE: People with learning disabilities, audiologists
PRICE: £50.00 + VAT; £200.00 + VAT (set of 4 videos)
PRODUCER: Bournemouth: Dorset Healthcare NHS Trust, 1996
DISTRIBUTOR: Viewpoint Project
This is one of a series of four videos that aim to show what happens during healthcare procedures to enable more effective communication by and with people with learning disabilities. Real people in real situations are used in the videos.
In *Let's test your ears*, David, a white man with a learning disability, visits an audiologist with his father. David thinks his hearing is all right but his father thinks that sometimes he can't hear. The audiologist sets up a series of games to check whether David can identify the source of a sound and what levels of sound he can hear. He makes an impression of David's ear for a hearing aid. This involves using a syringe to squeeze paste into the ear. The video then cuts to the next visit when David's hearing aid is ready. The audiologist shows him how to use it. David leaves, telling his father that he can hear better now.
The audiologist is reassuring and clear in his instructions to David. However, although we are shown the equipment he uses, he doesn't explain why he is using it or what he is hoping to discover. In the section showing him making an impression of David's ear, the video doesn't show the audiologist explaining that this is for a hearing aid or why David needs one.
There is a booklet that accompanies the series. Aimed at support workers and carers, this suggests how to use each video effectively and includes a number of

practical activities that can be used alongside it – for example, using objects of reference such as headphones or a hearing aid.

This resource would be useful in preparing people with learning disabilities for a visit to an audiologist. It could be used with people who have limited language skills as it communicates visually as well as through words. Because some of the action is not clearly explained, the video would need to be watched with a support worker. Some scenes will need supplementary information. It could also be used in training primary healthcare professionals and support workers, though not necessarily as an example of good practice.

Now it makes sense: let's test your eyes

FORMAT: Video, 15 mins; notes
AUDIENCE: People with learning disabilities, opticians
PRICE: £50.00 + VAT (single video); £200.00 + VAT (set of 4 videos)
PRODUCER: Bournemouth: Dorset Healthcare NHS Trust, 1996
DISTRIBUTOR: Viewpoint Project

This is one of a series of four videos that aim to show what happens during healthcare procedures to enable more effective communication by and with people with learning disabilities. Real people in real situations are used in the videos.

In *Let's test your eyes,* Brenda, a white woman with a learning disability, visits a hospital eye clinic with a support worker. The doctor asks her questions to assess her eyesight and general health. After checking that Brenda knows her letters, the doctor carries out a series of tests including using letter charts, picture charts, and 3D pictures. The eye specialist explains clearly what she wants Brenda to do for each test. Eye drops are administered by the eye specialist to dilate Brenda's pupils so that the back of her eyes can be examined in a darkened room. Brenda is told that she is shortsighted and is given a prescription for spectacles. Brenda goes to an optician to choose some frames, which she does, clearly expressing her likes and dislikes. The video then cuts to Brenda receiving her new glasses and saying she can now see better.

There is a booklet that accompanies this series. Aimed at support workers and carers, this suggests how to use each video effectively and includes a number of practical activities that can be used alongside it – for example, using objects of reference such as flashcards or optical equipment.

This resource would be useful in preparing people with learning disabilities for an eye test or to explore anxieties about procedures, such as using eye drops. It could be used with people who have limited language skills as it communicates both visually and through words. The video should be watched with a support worker. Some scenes will need supplementary information. It could also be used in training primary healthcare professionals and support workers.

Now it makes sense: seeing the dentist

FORMAT: Video, 15 mins; notes
AUDIENCE: People with learning disabilities, dentists, dental hygienists
PRICE: £50.00 + VAT (single video); £200.00 + VAT (for set of 4 videos)
PRODUCER: Bournemouth: Dorset Healthcare NHS Trust, 1996
DISTRIBUTOR: Viewpoint Project

This is one of a series of four videos that aim to show what happens during healthcare procedures to enable more effective communication by and with people

with learning disabilities. Real people in real situations are used in the videos.
In *Seeing the dentist*, Jonathan, a young white man with a learning disability, visits the dentist with his support worker. Prior to the visit, the support worker uses pictures to explain what will happen. In the waiting area, Jonathan says he hates going to the dentist. The support worker reminds him of the last time he came, showing him a picture of the dentist. We see Jonathan's initial dental check-up – the dentist examines his mouth and finds a tooth that needs filling. She cleans and polishes his teeth, helped by a dental nurse. The video then cuts to the second visit, when Jonathan has the filling. The dentist explains why he has to have a local anaesthetic. Before she fills the tooth, she shows him the equipment she is going to use and asks him for his consent. All parts of the dental examination and filling process are shown very clearly. The dentist is reassuring and explains what she is going to do and why before doing it. Jonathan's support worker sits in the background. Jonathan is calm throughout.
There is a booklet that accompanies the series. Aimed at support workers and carers, this suggests how to use each video effectively and includes a number of practical activities that can be used alongside it – for example, objects of reference such as a toothbrush or dental equipment.
This resource is suitable for both children and adults and would be useful in preparing people with learning disabilities for a visit to the dentist. It could be used with people who have limited language skills as it communicates visually as well as verbally. The gentle pace of the video allows plenty of time for the viewer to think about what is happening and to anticipate how she or he might react in a similar situation. It would need to be watched with a support worker as it could bring out people's fears and anxieties. The video could also be used in training primary healthcare professionals and support workers.

Now it makes sense: seeing the doctor

FORMAT: Video, 15 mins; notes
AUDIENCE: People with learning disabilites, general practitioners, primary healthcare team
PRICE: £50.00 + VAT (single video); £200.00 + VAT (for set of 4 videos)
PRODUCER: Bournemouth: Dorset Healthcare NHS Trust, 1996
DISTRIBUTOR: Viewpoint Project
This is one of a series of four videos that aim to show what happens during healthcare procedures to enable more effective communication by and with people with learning disabilities. Real people in real situations are used in the video.
In *Seeing the doctor*, Julie, a white woman with a learning disability, has earache. Her support worker explains that the doctor is coming to see her. We then see Julie's examination by the doctor, who introduces himself, asks her about her ear, and explains each intervention before he does it – we see him check her pulse, take her temperature, listen to her heart, take her blood pressure, and examine her mouth, eyes, and ear. He explains that since her ear is red, he will give her some tablets to make it better. Finally, he does a blood test. It is clear that Julie understands what he is going to do and what is required of her. Later, we see Julie taking her tablets. The video ends with Julie and her support worker in the garden. She is obviously better.
All parts of the examination, and the equipment the doctor uses, are shown very clearly. The doctor explains what he is going to do, but not why, except to make things better. Occasionally he uses

Makaton. Julie's support worker sits beside her throughout the examination, holding her hand and offering support where needed.

There is a booklet that accompanies the series. Aimed at support workers and carers, this suggests how to use each video effectively and includes a number of practical activities to use alongside it – for example, using objects of reference such as a thermometer or a stethoscope.

This resource would be useful in preparing people with learning disabilities before a visit to the doctor. It could be used with people who have limited language skills as it communicates visually as well as through words. It could also be used in training primary healthcare professionals and support workers.

The parenting series

FORMAT: Booklets (x5), 16-pages each; audio cassette
AUDIENCE: Parents and prospective parents with learning disabilities
PRICE: £10.00 inc. (single copy); £37.50 (for the set of five); £2.50 (for audio cassette)
AUTHOR: McGaw, S.
PRODUCER: Kidderminster: British Institute of Learning Disabilities (BILD), 1995
DISTRIBUTOR: BILD Publications, Plymbridge Distributors
ISBN: 1 873791 364/410/461/518/569

The BILD parenting series includes five booklets. See under their individual titles for a review of each book: *What's it like to be a parent?*; *Children need healthy food*; *Children need to be clean, healthy and warm*; *Children need to be safe*; and *Children need love*.

The Patient's Charter and you with signs and symbols

FORMAT: Pack, 97-pages, illustrated
AUDIENCE: People with learning disabilities and visual impairment
AUTHOR: Hull and Holderness Community Health NHS Trust
PRICE: Single copies free
PRODUCER: Hull: Hull and Holderness Community Health NHS Trust, 1995
DISTRIBUTOR: Two Ten Productions

This resource is an interpretation of the Patient's Charter using simplified language, photographs, symbols, and line drawings of Makaton signs. It is produced by Hull and Holderness Community Health NHS Trust in conjunction with the Makaton Vocabulary Development Project. The pack aims to help people with moderate to severe learning disabilities, those with a sight difficulties, and limited reading skills, access the information in the *Patient's Charter and you*. It highlights the rights and expectations of health consumers and includes sections on: Access; Hospital; Community; Ambulance; Dental; Optical; Pharmaceutical; General practioner; and Maternity services.

Each standard from the Patient's Charter is accompanied by a photograph and a simplified written version with symbols underneath. This is easy to understand and can be used by individuals with or without assistance. There are supplementary line drawings of Makaton signs for the key words, which are designed to prompt carers and supporters to sign as they explain the standard.

There are general guidelines for carers, support staff, and facilitators. This resource can be used to prepare an individual for a specific visit to one of the health professionals mentioned and to emphasise the patient's rights in the process. The materials can also be used to stimulate general discussion about medical and health care and help to raise the consciousness of people with more severe learning disabilities about their basic health rights.

The photographs of patients are of an older, white population, not specifically people with learning disabilities, and the health personnel are stereotypical male doctors and female nurses.

Peter's new home

FORMAT: Book, 72-pages, illustrated
AUDIENCE: Young people and adults with learning disabilities
AUTHOR: Hollins, S., Hutchinson, D. and Webb, B. (illustrator)
PRICE: £10.00 inc.
PRODUCER: London: St George's Mental Health Library, 1993
DISTRIBUTOR: Royal College of Psychiatrists, Book Sales
ISBN: 1 874439 01X

This colour picture book is one of the *Books beyond words* series is written by two consultant psychiatrists, and is aimed at young people and adults with learning disabilities to explore the emotional impact of moving home.

It tells the story of a man with learning disabilities who moves away from his parental home to live in a shared house. He talks things over with his parents before making a final decision and then enlists the help of his social worker to make the necessary arrangements. When he packs up his belongings to move, Peter wants to take his favourite chair. His father doesn't want him to take the chair at first but his mother says it will help him settle into his new place if he has some familiar things around him. The story shows the move and feelings of homesickness that follow. With the support of his new house-mates and his family, he is able to adjust to life in his new home. The homesickness comes and goes and is most difficult when Peter goes back to his parents' house to visit and then doesn't want to leave. The main characters in the story are white, although other characters who live in the same house are from black and minority ethnic groups, and another resident uses a wheelchair.

The pictures are very expressive and are designed to tell the story in their own right. The use of pictures without text allows for individual interpretation and this is a very straightforward but gentle way of working on an individual basis with a young person or adult with learning disabilities. At the end of the book there are short story lines to accompany the pictures for those who prefer a ready-made story.

The book could be particularly useful for anyone thinking about moving away from home or for someone who has recently moved and is feeling homesick. It might also help others living in a shared house to understand the feelings of someone who may be about to move in with them.

Piece by piece – a comprehensive guide to sexual health for people with learning difficulties

FORMAT: Pack – video, 60 mins; ring-binder file with notes and activity sheets, 68-pages
AUDIENCE: Young people and adults with learning disabilities
PRICE: £58.69 inc.; £29.38 (for schools, service user, and advocacy groups)
PRODUCER: London: West London Health Promotion Agency, 1994
DISTRIBUTOR: Pavilion Publishing Ltd

This pack is for adults and young people with moderate or severe learning disabilities. It aims to explore and encourage understanding of personal and sexual feelings and experiences. The pack assumes people have an understanding of the difference between male and female and between child and adult. The teaching aims are given as: providing clear information; placing it in a social and moral context; developing understanding of concepts such as privacy; and the development of confidence and social skills through active learning and role-play. There is a strong focus on private and public activity, on good feelings and self-assertion. The pack was developed by Image in Action who have extensive experience of this work.

The pack contains a sexually explicit video and a folder of extensive support material divided into five sections: naming and knowing body parts; masturbating; making choices (saying 'yes' or 'no'); loving each other; and having sex. Each of these sections relates to two of the ten scenes in the video, and every scene contains a number of learning areas. For example, scenes 1 and 2 name and identify different body parts and introduce the concepts of privacy and self-esteem. The pack advises that the sections are not plans for single sessions, but each one is likely to be the basis for several sessions.

A number of people introduce the video, including a woman with a learning disability who is very clear about the need for, and the purpose of, the pack and its empowering possibilities. The video uses three-quarter life-size puppets that are manipulated by adult puppeteers. This manipulation is at first disturbing but the clear aim and presentation of the material draws the viewer in. Puppets were chosen to avoid problems associated with pornography, voyeurism, and privacy. A section in the folder highlights the need to discuss the use of puppets and makes suggestions about how to do this. The eight puppets used include characters from black and minority ethnic groups. Heterosexual and same-sex relationships are portrayed.

The video is not designed to be used on its own, but as a visual reinforcement of the extensive material in the folder. The pack contains a wealth of ideas, activities, and discussion points for use with groups and individuals. These are tailored to varying levels of ability. For example, in the section on loving each other, one activity is to 'ask your group to suggest places that the couple might go to together and how they might spend the time together. You could make a collage of places they have been.' The activities raise a range of issues that can be drawn out by the facilitator; for example, the nature of relationships and the difference between friends and boyfriends or girlfriends, and distinguishing between 'good' and 'bad' touch.

Additional support material, mainly pictures, is required, and the bibliography suggests where these can be obtained. The pack does not cover topics such as puberty, contraception, conception, and the life cycle, but suggests other appropriate resources for this. Easy to use and clearly presented, this pack has been designed with care and attention and should support learning well.

Plan your day

FORMAT: Multi-media – resource file; illustrated guide, 58-pages; appointment book; card case; monthly pocket calendars; date cards (x84); choice cards (x48), illustrated; date number tabs (x31); marking set; phone directory cards (x2); display pages (x10); looseleaf sheets (x27), illustrated

AUDIENCE: People with learning disabilities

PRICE: £99.95 + VAT

PRODUCER: USA: Attainment Company

DISTRIBUTOR: Winslow Press

This undated resource provides a system for teaching individuals to plan and schedule daily activities and to keep

appointments. A facilitators' guide gives details of a three-step action plan for helping individuals to understand the notion of planning a sequence of events for each day and to plan daily and longer-term schedules with gradually increasing levels of independence.
A variety of items are included and users can select those which seem most useful – appointment book, display pages or card case (with slot-in cards representing leisure pursuits, work, college, and various activities in the home), stickers, photocopiable sheets, and pens. Produced in the USA, *Plan your day* sometimes uses language or activities that may be unfamiliar, such as baseball and 'prep rally'. However, most people will want to create their own cards appropriate to their personal needs and interests.
The time-keeping system involves training people to follow through a sequence of events around a key activity, such as lunch, and eventually to learn to match digital times written on cards to their digital watches so that they are learning to match numbers rather than learning to tell the time. 'People cards' can be created with photographs of people the individual knows well, with details of their address, phone number, and birthday. These cards can then be slotted into the appointment book to aid memory about who the individual is seeing and when.
A video shows how the system can be used, through the story of Carl and Jason who are always late and Mary who shows them how to use the 'Plan your day' system. The system is probably most useful to those who are developing an individualised timetable or who are moving towards greater independence. It is a long-term project which will involve thought and preparation, and it will be necessary to select those parts of the resource which seem most useful.

Play helps – toys and activities for children with special needs

FORMAT: Book, 186-pages
AUDIENCE: Parents, carers, early years workers
AUTHOR: Lear, R.
PRICE: £16.99 inc.
PRODUCER: Oxford: Butterworth Heinemann, 1986, 1993 (3rd edition)
DISTRIBUTOR: Heinemann Educational
ISBN: 0 7506 0572 3
This book is one of the *Play helps* series and is aimed at parents and carers of children with disabilities, although it contains ideas that can be used with all children. It covers a very wide range of abilities from children with a severe learning and physical disability to those who may be temporarily ill in bed. Although written for use by parents it could, for instance, be an invaluable resource in playgroups where there are disabled children. It is full of ideas for making simple but effective toys that do not involve spending much money. It also looks at how to provide sensory experiences for children.
The style is friendly and informative and includes case-studies, such as activities for children who have to remain permanently in bed, children with visual or hearing impairments, or children with a 'lazy' hand. It considers what features are needed in certain types of toy and how to adapt them to suit the needs of particular children. It also shows how to help a child get the most from a toy. The author encourages the reader to analyse the talents of the child and build on these.
The book is divided into five sections. Each section aims to build on and develop the skills the child has. There are individual and group activities, not all requiring supervision. The sections include: Making the most of sight; Making

the most of hearing; Making the most of taste (including how to help children who need to 'taste' everything); Making the most of smell (including how to create smelly toys and aromatic experiences); and Making the most of touch.
There are small black-and-white line drawings of toys and children and some small photographs. The appendix contains detailed lists of books for children with special needs, books about play for children of all ages, books for parents of children with special needs, specialist educational toy suppliers, play organisations, and other relevant groups.

A proper house

FORMAT: Video, 23 mins
AUDIENCE: People with learning disabilities
PRICE: £15.00 inc.
PRODUCER: Mid Glamorgan: Red Flannel Films, 1994
DISTRIBUTOR: Rhondda Community Support Team

This video features people with learning disabilities who live in Mid Glamorgan talking about moving into their own homes. First we are introduced to a middle-aged couple who, after many years of living in a hospital, moved into their own home in the community. When this happened they decided they wanted to live together. Both partners talk enthusiastically about how they enjoy having a home of their own and how important this is to them. They also speak about how the move has changed their lives, giving them more responsibilities such as household chores or shopping, and greater freedom – for example, being able to go out in the evenings and enjoy social activities. A care assistant talks about how each of them has grown in confidence and ability over the months since leaving hospital, and we see the couple enjoying an evening out at a social club in an inclusive environment.
The video moves on to three young women, each of whom used to live with their parents, who now live in a flat together. The women talk positively about being more independent and how they went about initiating the move: talking to their parents and to social workers and asking them to help organise it. One of the women says that a reason she wanted to move was because she was thinking of the future. Her parents were not very keen on the idea of her moving out at first but now can see the sense of it. One of the women is not able to speak and her father talks on the video on her behalf. He describes how she gave non-verbal signals to let them know she wanted to leave home and how much she seems to be enjoying her independence.
Finally we hear the story of a young man whose mother died. With the help of his sister, he fought other family members through the courts for his right to stay in the family home. He now lives there alone and talks about why he chose to carry on

living in this house rather than move into shared accommodation.

This video could be a useful resource for discussing various living options with people with learning disabilities and the responsibilities and rewards independent living can bring. It might also be used by housing staff, social workers, and other professionals to raise awareness of the benefits of independent living for people with learning disabilities. All the people shown are white.

The protection pack

FORMAT: Pack – A4 sequencing cards (x20); A4 'yes'/'no' cards (x14); A5 student story booklets (x9); notes, 8-pages
AUDIENCE: Young people and adults with learning disabilities, teachers, parents, support workers
PRICE: £39.95 + 10% p&p
PRODUCER: Cambridge: Learning Development Aids, 1994
DISTRIBUTOR: Learning Development Aids

The three sets of teachers' resources in this pack are intended to reinforce work being done on personal protection and social behaviour with young people and adults with severe learning disabilities. They were produced as a result of a project initiated by Nottinghamshire Education Authority. Staff at a Nottingham school identified the particular needs of young people with severe learning disabilities in relation to personal protection – a dearth of suitable materials for this group led to the production of these resources. The materials emphasise the need to make choices and think about situations within the context of social relationships. All the topics are clearly illustrated with black-and-white line drawings. Most of the pictures are of white children but there are some children from black and minority ethnic groups.

The facilitators' booklet clearly describes preparatory points and principles, explains the three resources, and gives sample lesson plans. A list of additional resources is included. One set of 20 A4-sized situation cards deals with three topics: acceptable toilet behaviour for girls and boys from babies to adulthood; appropriate bathing behaviour; and which bed it is appropriate to sleep in at different ages. All the cards raise the issue of privacy, appropriate behaviour, and autonomy.

The other set of 14 'yes'/'no' discussion cards show parents, friends, or strangers offering cuddles, sweets, drinks, or car rides. Participants can discuss the situations, how they feel, and whether the offer should be accepted. A game is also possible with three Makaton answer cards supplied.

There are nine teenage story booklets that are intended to be used in group work where there is an opportunity to interpret the situations presented and discuss feelings. Each booklet includes a short picture story with full-page drawings and three- to seven-word descriptions. They deal with situations where the central character is not happy with another person's behaviour – for example, unwanted physical contact or a photograph taken when not wanted. Three similar single-picture situations are included to supplement discussion of the main point together with the relevant Makaton symbols. Many ambiguous situations are included that will promote plenty of discussion. The pack is flexible and includes ideas for using the stories but does not prescribe a correct response.

Same as everyone else

FORMAT: Video, 14 mins
AUDIENCE: Adults with moderate learning disabilities
PRICE: £39.00 + VAT
PRODUCER: Liverpool: Liverpool Self-advocacy Group, 1994
DISTRIBUTOR: Boulton Hawker Films
This video was made by a group of adults with learning disabilities from the Liverpool Self-advocacy Group with support from the Advocacy Team. It begins with an explanation that the video is by, for, and about people with learning disabilities. The speaker says that they do not like to be labelled, but that 'learning difficulties' is a better term than most. There follows a series of interviews with members of the public, many of whom do not understand the term, confusing it with dyslexia or something to do with children. Some people interviewed do have greater knowledge of the term, which is explained in the video as referring to people who have difficulty learning and are denied access to education and other opportunities.
In much of the video, people with learning disabilities speak to camera, explaining how they want the same rights as everyone else – for example, the right to independence, education, and jobs. In role-plays, the group enact scenes about being treated like a child and about problems experienced when going to college. A social education centre is shown as a place where nothing changes and where people do piece-work and are bored.
This video could be used with groups of adults with moderate learning disabilities to trigger discussions about self-advocacy groups and why they are needed. There is no support material with the video.

Self-advocacy can lead you to ...

FORMAT: Pack: booklets (x4); poster
AUDIENCE: People with learning disabilities
PRICE: £2.50 inc. (poster only); £19.95 + 10% p&p (pack)
PUBLISHER: Nottingham: EMFEC, 1994
DISTRIBUTOR: EMFEC (poster and leaflets separately or together as a pack), Pavilion Publishing (pack only)
ISBN: 1 85258 249 9
This poster is part of *The self-advocacy pack*, which contains a set of booklets and posters about what self-advocacy means and how it should be supported. The other leaflets in the pack are aimed at parents, carers, service providers in education, and health and social services, and are entitled: *At home with self-advocacy*, *Living with self-advocacy*, *Whose learning*? and *Volunteering and self-advocacy*. These titles are reviewed separately in this book.
The poster is intended for 'members and supporters of self-advocacy groups and anyone who is interested in self-advocacy and empowerment.' It is set out like a map with a series of routes leading to different areas. At the end of each route, cartoon figures with speech balloons talk about self-advocacy and what it involves. The themes range from choosing what colour socks to wear to joining forces with other people to bring about change in service provision. In the centre of the map are the words 'self-advocacy can lead you to ...'. The main areas identified are: taking part in planning; trying new things; work; sticking up for yourself and your rights; being proud of who you are and what you can do; having a say about where you go in the day and what you do there; being part of strong groups and networks; direct action; and getting on with everyday life. On the back of the poster are some words of encouragement for self-advocacy groups

and a brief explanation of what the picture is about.
The poster is not really accessible to people without reading skills or with sight difficulties because it is wordy, the cartoon figures are small, and the drawings are not self-explanatory. But precisely because the picture is so detailed and busy, it is interesting and intriguing for those with good reading skills and good eyesight. It could also be read to people. The poster and booklets are available separately and together as a pack from EMFEC, and together as a pack only from Pavilion Publishing.

Sequential thinking: sets 2, 4, 5

FORMAT: Colour picture cards (3 sets from a set of 5)
AUDIENCE: Children and adults with learning disabilities
PRICE: £29.95 + 10% p&p + VAT (all 5 sets); £7.25 + 10% p&p + VAT (sets 2 & 4); £8.50 + 10% p&p + VAT (set 5)
PRODUCER: Cambridge: Living and Learning, 1993, 1994
DISTRIBUTOR: Learning Development Aids
LANGUAGES: English, German
The aim of the five sets of cards is to help children develop the ability to recognise and think in time sequences. Three of the sets could be used as resources for health-related education.
Set 2 contains 30 cards in six sequences: making gingerbread men (x4); cutting down a tree (x4); making a cup of coffee (x5); some events in a child's day (x5); a ball rolling into the road (x6); and a broken goldfish bowl (x6).
Set 4 contains 30 cards in six sequences of five cards: feeding birds; building a sand castle; going fishing; waiting for a bus; washing up; and picking flowers.
Set 5 contains 60 cards in nine sequences: a bird laying an egg (x6); washing a car (x6); doing the laundry (x6); going to bed (x6); going shopping (x6); painting a picture (x7); writing a letter (x7); putting up a shelf (x8); and a visit to the doctor (x8).
The cards are colourful and well drawn in the style of children's books. They are quite small which makes them handy but of little use for children with sight difficulties. They would need laminating as they are not very sturdy. Children from black and minority ethnic groups are included, but there are no drawings of children or adults with visible disabilities. There is a small leaflet with suggestions for using the cards with individuals or groups, including ideas about further activities – for example, children may wish to draw their own sequences. Exploring sequences of events in this way could be used to teach safety and accident prevention. The cards will be useful for teaching about before and after states as well as cause and effect. They can also be used to develop pre-reading skills and planning skills.
These are part of a five-set series, comprising a total of 180 cards.

Sex in context

FORMAT: Pack, 309-pages
AUDIENCE: Professionals working in schools or adult services, with people with profound and multiple impairment, parents and carers
AUTHORS: Craft, A. and Downs, C.
PRICE: £69.95 + p&p
PRODUCER: Brighton: Pavilion Publishing, 1997
DISTRIBUTOR: Pavilion Publishing Ltd
ISBN: 1900600552
This comprehensive pack was developed for working with staff in statutory and voluntary organisations, who care for someone with profound and multiple impairment, their parents, and carers. It is intended for use in school settings and adult services.

The aim of this innovative pack is to help staff develop approaches, strategies, and safeguards, within their services, relating to the sexuality of the children, adolescents, or adults who they support. It also sets out to extend to this group of people, the knowledge and experience that has been developed in working with people with mild to moderate learning disabilities in relation to their sexuality.
The pack consists of a handbook and two ringbinders. You are requested to read the handbook – *Safeguards in systems* – first, as it is essential for staff to feel supported and confident in their learning and practice. The handbook facilitates a review of service policies and the development of practical guidelines. It also contains lists of useful organisations to contact.
Part 1 contains strategies for devising Personal and Social Development Programmes and includes both staff exercises and learning activities for students and service users. Part 2 covers setting up programmes for individuals and preparing to work with parents and carers. There are lists of materials for each activity and helpful advice about using the materials with people who have sight difficulties.
It is important to work through each section of the manuals in turn and for all members of a staff team to attend consistently. Some of the exercises require skilled facilitation, preferably by an outsider, who is experienced in group work. There are notes for facilitators in each ringbinder.
There were 13 project groups involved in the development of this resource, and all materials were piloted and evaluated by other groups of children and adults. The original groups were selected as a representative example of the population of the UK, and the authors embrace the widest range of attitudes towards sexuality in a multi-faith, multicultural society. Staff are encouraged to uphold equal opportunities principles in their working environments.
The project was funded by the Joseph Rowntree Foundation and the Department of Health. *Sex in context* is dedicated to one of its authors, Ann Craft, who died in 1997 in the final stages of the production of this training pack.

Sexual health education. Children and young people with learning disabilities – a practical way of working

FORMAT: Pack, A4, illustrated
AUDIENCE: 11- to 19-year olds with learning disabilities, teachers, parents, carers
AUTHORS: Adcock, K. and Stanley, G.
PRICE: £15.00 + 5% p&p (10% discount for BILD members)
PRODUCER: Kidderminster: British Institute of Learning Disabilities (BILD), 1996
DISTRIBUTOR: BILD Publications, Plymbridge Distributors
ISBN: 1873791380
This pack, aimed at 11- to 19-year-olds with learning disabilities, their teachers, parents, and carers, provides basic information about male and female bodies, forming sexual relationships, and staying safe. It was produced collaboratively by BILD and Barnardos and was trialled with children and young people with learning disabilities.
The pack consists of facilitators' notes, teaching plans for 12 workshop sessions, photocopiable handouts for participants, and overhead projector (OHP) templates, plus an extensive annotated bibliography of resources. There are three core components to the teaching sessions: health and hygiene; keeping safe; and relationships. The topics include: sex

education groups; sex education as a process; developing practical teaching plans; and working with staff groups/parents.

The methods used are participatory, including warm-up and ice-breaker exercises, group games, role-play, and discussion. Facilitators will need experience in health education and in working with young people with learning disabilities. The course is designed to be presented over a period of three-and-a-half to four days, with a recall day approximately six weeks later. Some sessions may need modifying to suit participants' needs. There is an emphasis on the importance of using simple, practical methods of communicating messages to children and young people with learning disabilities.

The pack can be used with staff, carers, and parents who wish to develop skills in this area. It can also be used to work directly with groups of young people with learning disabilities in schools, colleges, and community settings. Access to a photocopier and OHP is required, and some activities require art materials and fabrics – for example, drawing and creating puppets.

The sexuality and sexual rights of people with learning disabilities: considerations for staff and carers

FORMAT: Booklet, 34-pages
AUDIENCE: Support staff and carers
AUTHOR: Cambridge, P.
PRICE: £5.00 + p&p
PRODUCER: Kidderminster: British Institute of Learning Disabilities (BILD), 1996
DISTRIBUTOR: BILD Publications, Plymbridge Distributors
ISBN: 1873791739

The aim of this booklet is to promote the sexual rights of people with learning disabilities by drawing together research findings and good practice in an accessible format for staff and supporters. It stresses that many of the sexual rights fought for in the wider society are still denied to people with learning disabilities, and it looks at how services can work to promote and safeguard these rights.

The booklet uses text only, with no pictures, and is divided into 10 sections. The introduction gives an overview of the law in relation to sex and people with learning disabilities. The remaining sections each cover a different area in which sexual rights are important: sexual abuse and exploitation; sexual expression and relationships; same sex relationships; sex education; HIV and sexual health; confidentiality, dignity, and respecting privacy; pornography and sexual aids; and reproduction and contraception. Each section explores how these issues impact on people with learning disabilities and ends with a statement of rights, such as the 'right to freedom from sexual abuse and to protection from services'. Suggestions are then made about the action services, support staff, and carers can take to put these rights into practice, and the individual responsibilities that go with these rights.

Included in the booklet are valuable guidelines for staff on putting rights into practice, for example on confidentiality. It is outspoken in its defence of rights, though it tends to be stronger on issues for men than for women. It ends with a list of references and resources that will be invaluable for staff, people with learning disabilities, and supporters wanting to explore these issues in more depth. A companion book, *Your rights about sex,* has been produced for people with learning disabilities.

Simply drugs – drug education without too much reading or writing

FORMAT: Pack, A4, 83-pages
AUDIENCE: 11- to 19-year-olds (Key Stages 3 and 4) and young people with learning disabilities
AUTHOR: Cohen, J. (ed.)
PRICE: £55.00
PRODUCER: Liverpool: Healthwise, 1997
DISTRIBUTOR: Healthwise Resource Department
ISBN: 1873460090
This drug education pack is aimed at 11- to 19-year-olds (Key Stages 3 and 4), including young people with learning disabilities. The aim of the pack is to increase knowledge and understanding of drug use and related issues, preferably as part of a planned drugs education programme. Although the pack states that it was designed for young people with varied levels of reading and writing abilities, the materials provided are mostly text. The focus of the materials is on written rather than non-verbal forms of communication, although facilitators are advised to be more imaginative.
The pack consists of an introduction, sets of learning activities, and appendices. The introduction provides guidance on using the pack, including supplementary activity such as using outside speakers and the Internet. The learning activities are organised in four sections: finding out what people know and feel about drugs; knowledge and understanding of drugs; attitudes towards drugs; and skills in drug-related situations. There are details of objectives, the resources required, method, and extension activities. The appendices include a list of resources and contact addresses, and information about drugs including drugs and the law.
A range of individual and participatory methods are used, including quizzes, questionnaires, a card game, case studies, and small and large group work. Some activities require additional resources such as information leaflets. Basic group facilitation skills are required. It may be used in schools, colleges, and youth and community settings.

Smoking awareness pack

FORMAT: Pack, 62-pages
AUDIENCE: Young people and adults with learning disabilities
PRICE: £29.95 + p&p
PRODUCER: Welwyn Garden City: Hertfordshire Health Promotion, Horizon NHS Trust, and East Hertfordshire NHS Trust, 1998
DISTRIBUTOR: Pavilion Publishing Ltd.

This pack explores in a lighthearted way the negative effects of smoking on health. It is a visual resource for use by facilitators working with young people and adults who have difficulty with written material. The pack was devised by Hertfordshire Health Promotion team in conjunction with Horizon NHS Trust and East Hertfordshire NHS Trust.

The pack has two aims. The first is to inform people about the effects of smoking on health and the second is to help people who want to give up. It can be used to educate and inform about smoking in general or to achieve the separate aims.

The first section describes the effects of smoking on health. This is done through a combination of cartoons and a wealth of statistical evidence about smoking-related illnesses and the costs to the individual and others. The strong anti-smoking message is put across in a methodical and down-to-earth way and should appeal to anyone wanting generally to improve their awareness.

The second section is a practical group work tool to help smokers who want to give up, using more cartoons backed up by an action plan that tackles the emotional as well as physical dependency involved. Among the techniques included are: keeping a diary of thoughts and feelings; getting support from others; and the use of nicotine replacement products. There are useful sections on how to recognise withdrawal symptoms and how to stay stopped.

The pack can be used with people with mild to moderate learning disabilities, and the illustrations of different races, genders, and abilities will appeal to a range of groups, although the print is not large enough to be accessible to people with sight difficulties. The pack can be used by professionals working in various settings: education; the health service; local authority; industry; and the voluntary sector.

A social/communication skills resource pack

FORMAT: Pack, 49-pages
AUDIENCE: Adults with learning disabilities
AUTHOR: Charters, C.
PRICE: £20.00 inc.
PRODUCER: Darlington: South Durham Health Care NHS Trust, 1994
DISTRIBUTOR: Durham County Priority Services NHS Trust

This pack consists of a ring-bound A4 folder. It contains 14 session plans taken from two social and communications skills training courses for adults with learning disabilities which were led by a speech therapist and an occupational therapist working within a community team for people with learning disabilities. Although it is a resource in its own right, users might wish to link it to a video, *The social scene*, also by Carole Charters, which uses a soap-opera format and can be used in conjunction with this pack.

An introduction gives a brief description of each of the people who participated in these courses (real names are not used). Social skills are defined by the authors as 'skills which are developed throughout our lives and which enable the individual to function as a socially acceptable member of our society.' The 13 sessions cover the following topics: initiating conversation; likes; dislikes; positive and negative feelings; body posture and facial expression; touch; proximity, choices, agreement, and disagreement; and social graces.

For each session, there is a list of objectives and a session plan typically involving discussion, role-play, video viewing, or using pictures from magazines. The materials involved are not supplied and will need to be sought out by the facilitator. Session plans consist of a brief list of activities. For example, the session on preferences (likes) suggests beginning with a recap of previous sessions, then introducing the subject of likes and dislikes. This is followed by a brainstorm of things that group members like and then each person makes a collage showing likes in the categories listed: food, clothes, holidays, and leisure. The group members then choose one category and discuss their choices. The same format is used for the other three categories. The session ends with tea, coffee, and an informal chat. Facilitators will need to plan their own sessions around the needs and abilities of their particular group. At the end of each session plan, the authors comment on what they observed during the sessions that they ran – for example, 'it was found that for some group members individual collages provided a very solitary activity with the opportunity for little verbal intervention. To counteract this, we would suggest a group collage for each category is made to help promote verbal and social interaction.'

Social star: 1 and 2

FORMAT: Pack – book 1, 488-pages, illustrated; book 2, 468-pages, illustrated
AUDIENCE: Children of primary age with special educational needs, teachers, support workers
AUTHOR: Gajewski, N., Hirn, P. and Mayo, P.
PRICE: £65.00 Book 1 and 2; £125.00 (3 books – Book 3 not reviewed here)
PRODUCER: USA: Thinking Publications, 1993, 1994
DISTRIBUTOR: Winslow Press
ISBN: 0930599799 Book 1; 0930599918 Book 2

This pack was developed for teachers and other professionals working with children in mainstream and special needs schools in the USA. It is described as an elementary curriculum for teaching social and communication skills and would be suitable for working with children of primary school age in the UK. The coursework is experiential, interactive, and requires literacy skills.

The resource outlines its aims clearly. It offers opportunities to apply and practise many new skills, including listening, communication, co-operation, and conflict resolution skills. The authors suggest that these skills will be needed in educational and employment settings. The approach focuses on strengths, rather than weaknesses, and encourages the use of new skills throughout the day.

This pack is part of a series. The two books reviewed are: book 1 *General interaction skills* and book 2 *Peer interaction skills*. Each book contains 15 units, an introduction, and appendices with clear photocopiable sheets. The material will need to be adapted for use with blind and partially sighted.

The courses are based on the day-to-day lives of six fictional children. The social interactions take place with each other and within their families, schools, and communities. Each unit is goal-related and contains information about the skills involved. This is followed by a series of lessons and activities, and suggested reading, some of which relates to learning disability. There are lists of materials and structured lesson plans. Each unit follows the same format, but the length varies. There are social skill ratings for assessing individual needs.

The language and artwork in this pack reflect mainstream America and the materials may require some adaptation. There are no disabled characters included in the action, but difference and diversity, especially relating to culture and religion, are given a high profile.

These courses do not have to be taught in their entirety and the pack includes strategies for adaptation. The authors stress the need to read the cognitive plan for each unit, to begin with the earlier units first, and to model all the skills embedded in the coursework. A third book, not reviewed, has recently been published to focus on nine more critical social skills such as settling conflicts, making an apology, and taking charge of anger.

Socially speaking

FORMAT: Pack, 149-pages, illustrated
AUDIENCE: Young people with mild to moderate learning disabilities, teachers, speech therapists, support workers
AUTHOR: Schroeder, A.
PRICE: £17.95 + p&p
PRODUCER: Wisbech: Learning Development Aids, 1996
DISTRIBUTOR: Learning Development Aids
ISBN: 185503252X
This book is aimed at teachers, speech therapists, and others working with mild to moderately learning disabled pupils in the classroom. It is a comprehensive social skills course intended to help pupils build effective communication and relationship skills and was piloted with at least one class of pupils aged 8–11 years. Literacy skills are needed for many of the activities and the materials would require some adaptation for use with blind and partially sighted pupils. It can be also be used with physically disabled children and small groups in mainstream education.
The programme covers a school year and includes three units of 12–13 sessions each. It is important to follow the programme through as each unit builds on the previous ones, and skills developed in Unit 1are pre-requisites for Unit 2. While each session follows a similar format, there is no guidance as to the length of the sessions. This will depend on the age and ability of the group.
Circle-time activities are used in mainstream education and the author has developed these tools in the light of the particular difficulties that learning disabled children may experience in their social interactions with others. The skills required for effective social interaction include the ability to listen to others, the use of receptive and expressive language, and problem-solving skills. The resource could be useful for developing self-advocacy and group skills.
Each session is well laid out with lots of clear photocopiable worksheets. Video and audio equipment are required. The activities could be used individually, outside the context of this programme, although the author points out that the well-structured format of the course helps pupils to feel secure and that real change takes time. The author, a speech therapist and teacher, has developed the course, over a period of six years.
The author suggests that social and cultural differences need to be considered when using some of the materials in this course – for example, the use of body language, especially eye contact.

Special needs and drug education

FORMAT: Pack – A4 binder; learning materials, 35-pages; leaflets (x6); laminated photographs (x30)
AUDIENCE: Young people and adults with learning disabilities, teachers, support workers
PRICE: £38.00 inc.; £12.00 for updated pages
PRODUCER: London: Richard Ives, 1995 with update 1998
DISTRIBUTOR: Richard Ives
This pack contains notes for facilitators, 35 photocopiable worksheets, and eight appendices. The latter include a list of

resources, organisations, and publications; a list of organisations in Hackney; plus information about the law on drugs prevention in the national curriculum, facilitating active learning, formulating a policy on drugs and solvents, guidelines from the National Curriculum Council, and basic information on drugs. The pack includes an order form for 25 laminated cards entitled 'Habit families'. The cards, reviewed elsewhere in this publication, can be used to play a number of games and activities described in the pack. Those who do not wish to pay extra for these could make their own cards using their own pictures or the photocopies of the cards provided. A number of leaflets about drugs and solvent abuse, aimed at parents, young people, and professionals, are also included. Seventeen group exercises are described. Each clearly sets out the purpose of the exercise, its relevance, and scope, and lists the materials and preparation needed. For example: 'learners will need to be able to formulate some words to describe feelings. You might find it useful to do Exercise 2 before you tackle this one'. The exercises are described in detail together with suggestions for adapting them according to the needs of different groups. Facilitators should be prepared to deal with a range of responses to the exercises and need to familiarise themselves with any policy on drugs operating within their school or centre. It would be helpful to have the names and addresses of local organisations that provide help and advice on this issue. Topics covered include: the things that make us feel good or bad; how drugs and alcohol change the way we feel; the strength of alcoholic drinks; peer pressure; legal and illegal drugs; risks involved in taking drugs; why people use drugs; finding alternatives to drug use; assertiveness skills; and people to go to for advice. Cartoon drawings used on worksheets include representations of black, white, and disabled young people. This comprehensive and versatile resource could be used with children or adults, although some of the worksheets that refer to 'girls' and 'boys' may need to be re-worded for use with adults. Many teachers and group facilitators will want to select exercises according to the needs of their group and the time they have available. The pack stresses the importance of placing drug education within a planned programme of learning about drugs which preferably includes other aspects of health and social education. Facilitators are advised that, 'One-off exercises about drugs, are unlikely to be helpful and may have the unfortunate effect of exciting learners' curiosity about drugs, without providing sufficient information for them to be aware of the risks and dangers.' The author updated the pack in 1998, which involved re-designing the pack and the inclusion of additional activities.

START! How to set up and run a self-advocacy group

FORMAT: Video pack – video, 23 mins; A4 booklet, 12-pages
AUDIENCE: Adults with learning disabilities
PRICE: Free (self-advocacy groups); £16.50 (small voluntary organisations); £41.50 (statutory sector)
PRODUCER: Newcastle upon Tyne: Speak for Ourselves/Dreamworld Productions, 1993
DISTRIBUTOR: Skills for People

This video was devised and presented by a group of people with learning disabilities who are members of a self-advocacy group in Newcastle. The video gives inspiration and guidance to those who may be thinking about setting up their own self-advocacy group. It is divided into clear, manageable sections so that it can be watched in stages. The quality of sound and picture is unusually good for this kind of self-made project and it is entertaining and humorous as well as being informative. The group includes men and women of varying ages. All the people shown are white.

The video explains how to set up a self-advocacy group in seven stages. It covers: getting people interested in joining, which looks at the reasons for joining a self-advocacy group, such as making friends, talking about things that matter to you, getting support from others, and trying new activities; advice about finding a suitable meeting space; finding an adviser who is helpful but doesn't try to run the group for you; deciding who should take the role of chairperson, secretary, treasurer, and any other jobs that might need to be done, such as a transport organiser or publicity officer; some ideas for raising funds; and finally information about some of the things the group can do, such as improving services, writing letters to the council, holding conferences, and so on. Members of the group talk enthusiastically about the benefits of joining a self-advocacy group.

The cartoon-illustrated booklet that accompanies the video summarises the main points made in the video and lists useful organisations that may be able to help and advise.

Sticking up for yourself: self-advocacy and people with learning difficulties

FORMAT: Booklet, 36-pages, illustrated
AUDIENCE: People with learning disabilities
AUTHOR: Simons, K.
PRICE: £4.20 inc. (£3.20 inc. for self-advocacy groups)
PRODUCER: Bristol: Joseph Rowntree Foundation/Norah Fry Research Centre, 1993
DISTRIBUTOR: Norah Fry Research Centre
ISBN: 0 9518171 8 3

This booklet was written by Ken Simons, a researcher at the Norah Fry Research Centre of Bristol University. He interviewed members of three self-advocacy groups in Avon to find out what self-advocacy meant to them and what they thought of the services they used. The booklet aims to enable people with learning disabilities to think about self-advocacy. It begins by looking at the general issue of why self-advocacy skills are necessary and then looks at the specifics of how such a group might be set up and how it might be run. Each of the three self-advocacy groups described is organised in a different way: one is a day centre committee; one is a People First group; and one meets in the evenings at a different centre from the one its members attend. The booklet points out that many types of self-advocacy groups exist. It goes on to address some of the 'pros' and 'cons' of different groups, reinforced by the use of funny cartoons.

The booklet is written in simple terms and uses a lot of quotes from people with learning disabilities interviewed in the survey. For example, in a section about individual planning, comments include: 'I don't like them talking about my moods or bad temper' and 'They had different opinions about me ... Well they sort of said, "She can't do this or that".' These quotes are followed up by a series of questions and suggestions for people reading the book to think about, such as: 'Not everybody wants to have an IPP [individual programme plan]. Do you have a choice?' or 'What are IPPs like in your area? Good or bad? Try telling the people running the IPPs what you think.'

One section looks at labelling, rejecting both 'learning disability' and 'mental handicap' in favour of the term 'learning difficulties'. Another section of the book addresses the specific issue of the use of 'advisers' – their role and potential value to a group.

Overall the booklet represents an extremely useful introduction, in simple terms, to many of the most crucial issues around self-advocacy, its values and potential benefits. It could be used to enable people to compare their own feelings about self-advocacy with the wide range of comments by those who participated in the research. It is unusual in the detail with which it addresses the mechanics of running a group. Its basic message is: 'If you really want to find out about self-advocacy join your own local group, or if there isn't one, get together and set up your own.'

Taking self-advocacy seriously

FORMAT: Pack, 39-pages, illustrated
AUDIENCE: Service providers, voluntary groups
AUTHOR: Dawson, P., and Palmer, W.
PRICE: £6.00 inc.
PRODUCER: Nottingham: EMFEC, 1993
DISTRIBUTOR: EMFEC
ISBN: 185258226X

This pack is an introduction to the key principles and implications of self-advocacy for managers in health, social services, education, and voluntary organisations. It challenges managers to work through their perceptions of the difficulties and problems that organisations can encounter when encouraging people with disabilities to stand up for their rights. It offers advice and inspiration and uses materials from training courses where groups of service users and providers worked together to share their experiences and perceptions.

There are three parts. The first, 'What self-advocacy is about', includes a list of definitions from service users themselves with answers to some of the myths and barriers that are commonly put up by managers and others. 'Self-advocacy at work', looks at self-advocacy in action. There are examples of what groups of people want and can do to promote themselves, including writing charters, being consulted on planning, and making presentations. There is advice on how people can participate in aspects of service delivery including assessments, policy making and planning, and guidelines for sharing information and joint learning. *Taking self advocacy seriously* sets out a useful table encompassing all previous advice into an evaluation tool.

This pack could be used by social and support workers as core training material, or be used to inform claims for funding for self-advocacy projects. The information is clear, concise, and practical; just the kind of resource busy managers might have time for.

Talkabout: a social communications skills package

FORMAT: Pack, 161-pages, illustrated
AUDIENCE: Children and adults with learning disabilities, teachers, therapists
AUTHOR: Kelly, A.
PRICE: £32.50 + p&p
PRODUCER: Bicester: Winslow Press, 1996
DISTRIBUTOR: Winslow Press
ISBN: 0863881467

Talkabout is a pack designed to be used with children or adults with social communications skills difficulties. It was initially piloted with adolescents with mild learning disabilities at a college of further education. The resource aims to help therapists or teachers run social skills groups in a structured way. It covers: self awareness; communication skills; body language; advance paralinguistic skills; conversational skills; and assertiveness. The pack begins with an assessment procedure that enables a facilitator to evaluate an individual's self-awareness and awareness of others through interview and self-assessment. On completing this assessment, the facilitator can decide at which point of the ensuing six levels the individual should begin working.

Each of the six levels concerns a particular aspect of communication, starting with self and general awareness, moving through general communications skills within a group, body language, talking, and conversational and assertiveness skills.

Each level is explained clearly and includes well-designed photocopiable worksheets with a combination of simple written questions and cartoon illustrations. Level 1, for example, contains 20 worksheets that aim to improve awareness of self and others. The worksheets cover physical appearance (what do we look like?), personality (what are we like?), people in our lives, likes and dislikes, strengths and weaknesses (what are we good at and not so good at?), and problem solving. There is also a worksheet to enable participants to sum up what they have learned from this level. The pack suggests that the level could be spread over 20 sessions or adapted for fewer.

Other levels follow a similar format. Level 2 allows clients to assess their own communication skills and decide which level to work on next. Level 3 covers body language, and level 4 aims to improve paralinguistic skills. Levels 5 and 6 cover conversational and assertiveness skills respectively. Those using the pack are encouraged to add new worksheets and change the order of worksheets according to an individual's needs. It is suggested that some levels can be used in isolation.

Talkabout is an imaginative resource, which provides a wealth of material for facilitators working on social and communications skills, whether with individuals or groups. Those with limited reading skills will need support to complete the worksheets.

Talking inclusion

FORMAT: Cassette, 30 mins; worksheet, 4-pages; A3 colour poster
AUDIENCE: Professionals, parents, and support workers
PRICE: £5.00 inc.
PRODUCER: Bristol: Centre for Studies on Inclusive Education, 1994
DISTRIBUTOR: Centre for Studies on Inclusive Education

Talking inclusion is an audio cassette that contains interviews with children and young people about the education of disabled children within mainstream schools. The children are from Leeds, Sheffield, and London. It was produced by the Centre for Studies on Inclusive Education. They include children with physical disabilities, sensory disabilities, medical conditions, learning disabilities, and emotional difficulties.

The tape is divided into three sections: The practice of inclusion, where children talk about how ordinary schools cope with a wide range of needs; The good school guide, about what makes a good school from the young people's perspective, including comments on bullying; and The right to belong, where the interviewees talk about friendship and what they think about special schools. The accompanying workbook suggests topics for further debate and gives statistical information.

The resource is primarily aimed at professionals, parents, and groups involved in implementing the Special Needs Code of Practice required by all schools under the 1993 Education Act, but sections of the tape, such as those on bullying and on children's opinions of special schools, could be used to stimulate discussion about these subjects in groups of adults or young people with moderate learning disabilities.

Together we can get what we want

FORMAT: Book, 40-pages, illustrated
AUDIENCE: People with learning disabilities, service providers
PRICE: £2.00 + p&p
PRODUCER: Kidderminster: British Institute of Learning Disabilities (BILD), 1995
DISTRIBUTOR: BILD Publications, Plymbridge Distributors
ISBN: 1873791968
This book was prepared by service users and providers in the West Midlands. It is aimed at people with learning disabilities and the staff who work with them. The book explores how service users can have a say in service provision.
There are eight sections covering: showing respect for people; how to have your say; choosing staff; having a voice in service provision; assessment; taking part in monitoring and quality assessment; and running things for ourselves. The final section looks at where to get help and gives a list of resources and contact numbers. These are national and not just Midlands based.
Cartoon images and large text and simple sentences are used to give an accessible guide to how service users can make their views about services heard. The images are often humorous and the book is full of practical advice – for example, suggesting five steps to develop skills in interviewing and choosing new members of staff. It includes sections on what service users have said they want from staff and service planners. Images of black and Asian service users and staff are shown.
The book could be used with groups of people with learning disabilities to encourage self-advocacy and service user involvement. It will also be a useful resource for planners and providers to suggest ways in which services could take more account of the views of people with learning disabilities.
This resource was produced by Service User Groups in the West Midlands with assistance from the West Midlands Learning Disability Forum. It was funded by the Department of Health.

Understanding death and dying

FORMAT: Pack – booklets (x3), 21-pages, 24-pages, and 16-pages
AUDIENCE: People with learning disabilities, parents, carers, healthcare professionals
AUTHOR: Cathcart, F.
PRICE: £10 inc. for the set
PUBLISHER: Kidderminster: British Institute of Learning Disabilities (BILD), 1994
DISTRIBUTOR: BILD Publications, Plymbridge Distributors
ISBN: 1 873791 06 2
This pack was written by a clinical psychologist with experience of working with people with learning disabilities. The author became interested in the problems of dying and bereaved people and those of their carers when working in a general hospital. It includes a booklet that can be used either to help someone with a learning disability through the grieving process or to trigger discussion about death and dying. It could be used with an individual or in a group setting. In simple words and clear two-colour illustrations, it looks at the feelings people experience when they lose something; feelings like sadness, anger with themselves or others, guilt, blame, and learning to live without the thing they have lost. The book moves on to deal with feelings when a friend or someone close moves away and the individual has less contact with them or even no contact at all.

There is a brief and simple explanation of what death is, which tells the reader that people and animals die for different reasons, such as illness or accidents or because their bodies have become very old and therefore stopped working. It is simply stated that people have different ideas about what happens to people after they die, but that in all cases they cannot see, hear, or do things and the body does not work any more. Cremation and burial are explained in a few sentences and the reader is reassured that the dead person does not feel anything. The second half of the book looks at the process of grieving, commonly experienced thoughts, feelings, and anxieties, with the emphasis on the individuality of each person's experience and reassurance that unhappy feelings lessen over time. Throughout the book, the illustrations include people from black and minority ethnic groups.

Two other booklets accompany this resource. One is for families and friends, and the other for carers and other professionals. Both offer advice and suggestions about talking to people with learning disabilities about death and dying and involving them in visits to a dying person, funerals, or other rituals such as laying flowers or preparing food for people who come to offer condolences. They stress that the feelings and needs of a person with a learning disability are likely to be similar to those of other members of the family. The book for professionals also looks at coping with the death of someone with a learning disability. People with learning disabilities are often taught about growing up, sex, and relationships, but rarely does education explore ageing and death. The author urges facilitators to talk about death and bereavement before it happens and to include this in a general course.

Video first

FORMAT: Pack, 24-pages, illustrated
AUDIENCE: People with learning disabilities
PRICE: £4.00
PRODUCER: Bristol: Norah Fry Research Centre, 1993
DISTRIBUTOR: Norah Fry Research Centre (cheques payable to University of Bristol)
ISBN: 0951817191

This book was produced to help people with a learning disability, particularly those belonging to self-advocacy groups, make their own video. It begins by suggesting various reasons for using video for self-advocacy and comes up with some ideas for people to think and talk about.

There are step-by-step instructions that will help a group to plan and make their video, including making a storyboard, using camera equipment, sound, and editing. There are some important rules about using video and a section on how to stay safe. There is a useful section on further reading and places to go for more information.

The text in this book is simple and fairly large and it is illustrated with clear black-and-white drawings. These show people using a video camera (including someone in a wheelchair), equipment, and techniques. Some of the drawings include people from black and minority ethnic groups.

It is important for any group setting out to make a video to have someone who is experienced in using video equipment to help them. The book is organised as a structured programme but does not suggest how long each stage might take. This would depend on the abilities of the particular group.

This book was produced as part of the Norah Fry Research Centre 'Centre Shot Project' and supported by the Joseph Rowntree Foundation.

Volunteering and self advocacy

FORMAT: Booklet, 39-pages
AUDIENCE: Volunteers
PRICE: £1.50 inc.
PRODUCER: Nottingham: EMFEC, 1994
DISTRIBUTOR: EMFEC
This short booklet is part of a series devoted to self-advocacy that was produced by EMFEC in conjunction with organisations for volunteering in Derby and Nottingham. It is a pocket book aimed at people who have just become volunteers and is designed to help them think through their motivation and understand their role. The booklet offers definitions of the key principles underlying self-advocacy, discusses the role of the supporter, and teases out issues of equality, power, and control between volunteer and person. There is a helpful list explaining what self-advocacy is and is not, plus a reading list and details of other organisations to contact for further help.
This booklet would be a useful starting point for anyone becoming a volunteer, whether with a self-advocacy group or with individuals. The print, however, is too small to be of use to people with sight difficulties.

What a carry on: a video about basic first aid for people with learning disabilities

FORMAT: Video pack – video, 20 mins; notes, 9-pages; A4 laminated sheets
AUDIENCE: Young people and adults with learning disabilities
PRICE: £50.00 + VAT
PRODUCER: Leicester: 27A Access Artspace, 1998
DISTRIBUTOR: Pavilion Publishing Ltd
This resource contains a video with written script and worksheets. It looks in a lighthearted way at some basic aspects of first aid without pretending to deal with the subject comprehensively. The package was produced by 27A Access Artspace Ltd in conjunction with Coalville Resource Centre and funded by Leicester City Council Health Promotion Unit and Leicester Crimebeat.
The video features four young, white, disabled actors with able-bodied people in supporting roles. It is fun to watch and deals with five areas of first aid in an accessible way, including: how to cope with burns; fractures; cuts; electric shocks; and choking. It covers issues such as anxiety and reassurance. The information is shared through the story of four people with a learning disability who go to an activity centre for a weekend holiday. During this time several accidents occur to the able-bodied helpers. They require first aid treatment and this is provided by the young people with learning disabilities. The message in the video is positive as it shows the people with learning disabilities to be competent, caring, and full of common sense, whereas the staff and visitors are accident prone and fallible.
The package is intended for support workers to use with groups of people with learning disabilities as a stimulus for discussion and training. There are separate worksheets for each first aid topic covered. These provide clear advice on how to treat the accident, together with future safety tips. The script could be used for role-play exercises by the group itself or as a play put on for other groups of people. Support workers are encouraged to set up a more comprehensive first aid course. The pack should have a wide appeal, and could be used as part of a general course on health, to help prepare people for independent living, or as a teaching resource for frontline healthcare workers. The programme is well-structured and could be used as an audio resource for blind and partially sighted people.

What can I do if I'm arrested?

FORMAT: Video, 15 mins
AUDIENCE: People with learning disabilities, criminal justice services
PRICE: £28.00 or £25.00 to advocacy groups
PRODUCER: Rotherham: Speakup Self-Advocacy, 1995
DISTRIBUTOR: Speakup Self-Advocacy
This video is one of a series produced by Speakup, a self-advocacy group in Rotherham. It shows what can happen if the police arrest you and how to ask for a solicitor and an appropriate adult to help the solicitor. Other titles in the series include *How to go into hospital* and *Living safely*. All of the videos are devised by people with learning disabilities and aim to make information more accessible.
What can I do if I'm arrested? begins as the police are called to a car park where Jason, a young man with a learning disability has been seen trying car door handles. Jason is arrested and the remainder of the video is a step-by-step guide showing what happens to him up to his first police interview. Jason is shown being taken to the police station, being charged, having his rights explained to him, making contact with an 'appropriate adult' and a solicitor, and being interviewed. Jason's exchanges with police, solicitor, and appropriate adult are shown at length, giving the viewer time to understand the kinds of questions that could be asked. A voice-over (by a person with a learning disability) stresses the rights of people with learning disabilities to a solicitor and to the presence of an 'appropriate adult'. It advises them to tell the police that they have a learning disability and not to say they understand if they don't.
At the end of the tape there is a brief interview with the actor who played Jason. He recounts how, since making the video, he was arrested for something he did not do. He talks about the experience, saying that he 'cried a lot' and that he asked for a solicitor and an appropriate adult.
Some terms used in the video, such as 'solicitor' and 'appropriate adult', may need to be explained further either before or after screening. All the participants in the video are white, and the professionals involved play themselves.
The video would be a useful tool to inform individuals or groups about their rights if arrested. Although no clear pause points are indicated on screen, each step in the process of the arrest could be used to trigger discussion both about what can happen after an arrest and about the feelings people might experience when arrested (fear, shame, confusion), and how these could affect someone's behaviour in custody.

What's it like to be a parent?

FORMAT: Booklet, 16-pages, illustrated
AUDIENCE: Parents with a learning disability
PRICE: £10.00 inc. or £37.50 for the series set; audio-tape £2.50 extra
AUTHOR: McGaw, S.
PRODUCER: Kidderminster: British Institute of Learning Disabilities, 1995
DISTRIBUTOR: BILD Publications, Plymbridge distributors
ISBN: 1 873791 36 4
This is the first book in the BILD parenting series. There are five titles written by Sue McGaw of the Special Parenting Service, which works with parents with learning disabilities. The remaining four titles are listed under their individual titles: *Children need healthy food; Children need to be clean, healthy and warm; Children need to be safe;* and *Children need love*. The aim of the series as a whole is to identify, simplify, and teach the skills needed to be a parent.

What's it like to be a parent? is aimed at parents or prospective parents with learning disabilities. The 16-page booklet combines text with colourful pictures. It asks people to consider whether they are ready to be a parent and provides an introduction to some of the responsibilities of parenthood. Because the book contains many pictures, non-readers may find that they can look at these and remember some of the things they discussed when reading the book previously with the help of a facilitator.

The booklet contains information about the food babies and children need at different ages and the things they should not eat. There is advice about keeping children clean and making sure that their clothes and home are also clean and warm so that they have a better chance of staying healthy and of making friends. Two pages look at safety inside and outside the home with a 'spot the dangers' exercise. The book also shows some of things children need to learn, such as playing with toys, making friends, brushing their teeth, reading, playing sports, and so on. It stresses the importance of showing children love with words, smiles, and hugs when they've done well and teaching them how to behave. Finally the book looks at how parents cope with all this responsibility and how they need time to relax. It reassures parents that it is OK to call on others for help when needed.

The booklet could also be used with non-parents to trigger discussion about what being a parent involves. Although designed for individuals, it could be used in group settings.

When dad died

FORMAT: Book, 60-pages, illustrated
AUDIENCE: Young people and adults with learning disabilities
AUTHOR: Hollins, S., Sireling, L. and Webb, B. (illustrator)
PRICE: £10.50 inc.
PRODUCER: London: St George's Hospital Mental Health Library, 1989, 1994 (2nd edition)
DISTRIBUTOR: Royal College of Psychiatrists, Book Sales
ISBN: 1 874439 06 0

This colour picture book was written by two consultant psychiatrists and is part of the *Books beyond words* series for people with learning disabilities. It is intended for young people and adults with learning disabilities who have recently been bereaved or are grieving.

The 27 illustrations tell the story in a simple but meaningful way of a father who becomes ill and is taken to hospital where he subsequently dies. The pictures show the grief of the family, the reactions of different individuals to the death, the body in the coffin, the cremation, and ends on an optimistic note with the family coming to terms with their bereavement. The book uses a white family and is non-denominational. Another book in the series (*When mum died*) illustrates the death of the mother and burial rather than cremation. At the back of the book are short story lines to accompany the pictures for use if a facilitator assisting the reader wishes to use them. The book aims to inform about death and grief reactions, and to help people express their own feelings. It could also be used to explain the concept of death to those who have not yet experienced the loss of someone close to them.

The story begins and ends with the family album and readers are encouraged to use their own albums later. The use of pictures without text allows for individual interpretation and this is a very straightforward but gentle way of working on an individual basis with a young person or adult with learning disabilities.

When mum died

FORMAT: Book, 60-pages, illustrated
AUDIENCE: Young people and adults with learning disabilities
AUTHOR: Hollins, S., Sireling, L. and Webb, B. (illustrator)
PRICE: £10.00 inc.
PRODUCER: London: St George's Mental Health Library, 1989, 1994 (2nd edition)
DISTRIBUTOR: Royal College of Psychiatrists, Book Sales
ISBN: 1 874439 06 0

This colour picture book was written by two consultant psychiatrists and is part of the *Books beyond words* series for people with learning disabilities. It is intended for young people and adults with learning disabilities who have recently been bereaved or are grieving.

The 27 illustrations tell the story in a simple but meaningful way of a mother who becomes ill and is taken to hospital, where she subsequently dies. The pictures show the grief of the family, the reactions of different individuals to the death, the body in the coffin, the burial, and ends on an optimistic note with the family coming to terms with their bereavement. The book uses a white family and is non-denominational; another book in the series (*When dad died*) illustrates the death of a father and cremation rather than burial. At the end of the book are short story lines to accompany the pictures for use if a facilitator assisting the reader wishes to use them. The book aims to inform about death and grief reactions, and to help people express their own feelings. It could also be used to explain the concept of death to those who have not yet experienced the loss of someone close to them.

The story begins and ends with the family album, and readers are encouraged to use their own albums later. The use of pictures without text allows for individual interpretation and this is a very straightforward but gentle way of working on an individual basis with a young person or adult with learning disabilities.

Where can I go for help?

FORMAT: Video, 25 mins
AUDIENCE: People with learning disabilities
PRICE: £25.00 (advocacy groups), £28.00 (other groups)
PRODUCER: Rotherham: Speakup Self-Advocacy, 1999
DISTRIBUTOR: Speakup Self-Advocacy

This is one of a series of videos produced by Speakup, a self-advocacy group in Rotherham. It was made in conjunction with the Citizens' Advice Bureau. All of the videos are devised and acted by people with learning disabilities and aim to make information more accessible to this audience. This video is about how to access a wide range of voluntary agencies that offer advice and support for various problems.

The video follows the actors as they seek help and shows a variety of agencies available to them. In each agency there is a snapshot of an assessment interview. This is informative and encouraging to those involved and a voice-over explains what kind of problems can be helped.

The issues covered in the video include: benefits advice from the CAB; help with relationships from Relate; the Samaritans listening to a problem of depression; advice about courses and jobs from a student counsellor; victim support for people who have been burgled; Cruse offering a listening ear and a drop-in centre for a bereaved relative; and agencies such as Concern, which provide practical help with alcohol and drug misuse.

The video promotes the message that support is available if you need it, whatever the problem, and that the local community is a helpful place with agencies willing and able to help. It also demonstrates that there are many other people besides immediate support staff who can help with personal and private problems.

The video can be used by self-advocacy groups or support staff in a number of ways to help people with learning disabilities access local facilities. It can form the basis of discussions and research on personal problems and how to deal with them, and can play a useful part in courses on independent living or preparing individuals for moving into the community. The video could be used as an audio resource for blind and partially sighted people, although help would be needed to access local telephone numbers where necessary.

Whose learning? Self-advocacy and empowerment in education and training

FORMAT: Book, 47-pages
AUDIENCE: 16+ years with learning disabilities, further education and higher education professionals, parents, carers
PRICE: £6.00 inc.
PRODUCER: Nottingham: EMFEC, 1994
DISTRIBUTOR: EMFEC
ISBN: 1 852582 53 7

This booklet is aimed at managers, teachers, tutors, and others involved in the planning and provision of education and training for people over 16 years of age with a disability. It is a resource that can be used in colleges, schools, community education schemes, day and residential services, and training and voluntary organisations. It would also be helpful for parents and carers who support someone using, or wishing to use, education and training services. The booklet sets out to identify the thinking and practical steps that will encourage self-advocacy and empowerment in education and training organisations.

One of a series of publications about self-advocacy, the book is divided into three sections. Section 1 helps the reader to think about what education and training is for and the ways in which self-advocacy and empowerment can support the learning process. It outlines the many changes that are taking place in the funding and provision of these services and the opportunities and challenges that this presents.

Section 2 raises general issues about policy-making and planning. It explains the five stages of the learning process and shows how choice and participation can be a part of each stage. The stages are: finding out, induction, taking part, monitoring and assessment, and moving on.

Section 3 provides information on regional and national organisations that promote self-advocacy, education and training organisations, selected reading, and further training resources.
The text and black-and-white drawings are small and would be unsuitable for people with sight difficulties. There is no reference to equal opportunities in relation to cultural differences and the drawings are all of white people.
This booklet can be used as a source of information, a staff training handbook, or a tool for evaluating the quality of a provision. It was funded by the Department of Health and published by EMFEC. It was developed with input from college staff, students, and people from community education schemes, and reflects some of their concerns about self-advocacy and empowerment in education and training.

The work experience health and safety survival kit: all the essentials of student safety and placement selection

FORMAT: Pack – 140-pages, illustrated; leaflet *5-steps to risk assessment,* 6-pages; teachers' guide, 49-pages, illustrated, tables; *Special educational needs* supplement
AUDIENCE: 16- to 19-year-olds, with section for young people with learning disabilities
PRICE: £45.70 inc.
PRODUCER: Tetford: Integral Developments for RightTrack, 1996 (revised edition)
DISTRIBUTOR: RightTrack
ISBN: 0953417700
This pack contains information on health and safety issues to prepare students for work experience placements. It is suitable for use with 16- to 19-year-olds and is targeted at all young people. A supplement on special educational needs addresses the specific needs of students with physical and learning disabilities. The aim is to enable teachers to select suitable workplace experience placements for students and provide evidence of adequate health and safety preparation for these. Included in the pack are a teachers' guide, learning materials, and additional materials. The teachers' guide contains an introduction, checklists, activity guidance, exercises, and a progress check. The learning materials include: 10 generic sections on aspects of health and safety in the workplace; 7 industry-specific sections covering aspects specific to those industries; activities for students to carry out; and reminders of the main points of each section for photocopying as handouts or overhead projector (OHP) transparencies. The additional materials include: a colour OHP transparency on safety signs; a Health and Safety Executive leaflet *5 steps to risk assessment*; and a *Special educational needs* supplement (1995). The latter addresses issues around identifying placements for students with physical and learning disabilities, designing placement periods, and preparing students to gain as much as possible from their experience of the working environment.
The pack uses a range of individual and participatory methods with an emphasis on research and project work. It requires basic group facilitation skills, but is intended to be a flexible resource. Activities usually require students to go and find out something around the school or workplace, or on their way home or while out shopping. Activities should usually be completed over several days. The pack can be used in schools and colleges.
Health and safety legislation changes continually and the producers do provide updates on health and safety legislation from time to time. To keep up to date with the changing legislation, users can also

access the following website: www.workexperience.co.uk, designed by Anthony Johns, Simulus Education Services Ltd.

You and me – whole body movement teaching video

FORMAT: Video, 140 mins; illustrated colour guide 10-pages; set of 20 illustrated colour cards
AUDIENCE: Children, young people, and adults with learning disabilities
AUTHOR: Gunstone, M.
PRICE: £65.00 inc.
PRODUCER: Camforth: You and Me Yoga Centre, 1993
DISTRIBUTOR: You and Me Yoga Centre
This is an excellently adapted resource that demonstrates a system of yoga techniques using sound, colour, and 'whole body movement'. The programme is based on a sequence of yoga postures, each grouped by colour-coded body areas. The two-and-a-half hour video provides an enthusiastic introduction to the programme by the facilitators and participants, convincingly demonstrating why it has proved beneficial. It then shows the different groups doing each of the postures in turn. The groups range from young children to adults and include people with profound and multiple disabilities.
There are accompanying display cards for each posture. One side has a line drawing of someone demonstrating the posture, while the reverse lists the benefits of the posture and includes health cautions. The colour-code guide explains the coding system, and has teaching notes in the front. The whole pack has been very thoughtfully and effectively designed – for example, showing moderated techniques for people with restricted movement and incorporating extra communication aids for children with autism.
The participants shown all seem to enjoy and be absorbed in the programme; but it would have improved the video to have had more of their views. Other limitations of the resource are the choice of groups, which only have white participants, and the poor technical quality of some parts of the video. Guidance is not given about which postures to use when or in which order. However, a considerable strength of the pack is that it can be used with most people without needing further expert input.
It is suitable for day and residential services as well as schools and leisure facilities. It is shown in use at a local community centre, and the programme could be introduced in local sports, health, and adult education centres.

You, your body and sex

FORMAT: Video pack – video, 15 mins; notes, 17-pages, illustrated
AUDIENCE: Young people with moderate or severe learning disabilities
PRICE: £50.00 + VAT
PRODUCER: London: Life Support Productions, 1993
DISTRIBUTOR: Life Support Productions
This animated video aims to support general sex education for people with learning disabilities. It is accompanied by brief viewing notes plus a list of further resources. The video states that it should be viewed with a parent or carer. It is probably more appropriate for young people with moderate or severe learning disabilities. Older people may not identify with the young characters.
Two white characters, Kylie and Jason, are used to illustrate differences between male and female and child and adult, personal hygiene, male and female masturbation, heterosexual relationships, and sex. There is no mention of gay or lesbian relationships. The video moves fairly

quickly through these topics. The script is simple with repetition but some words may need further explanation such as 'discharge' or 'intimate'. Safer sex and condom use are strongly promoted, but it only refers to heterosexual intercourse. Facilitators will need to ensure it is understood that men who have sex with men also need to practise safer sex. Similarly, the video firmly states you can say 'no' to unwanted sex or sexual attention but only shows a woman saying 'no' to a man. Facilitators will need to cover this more fully so that men understand that they too can say 'no'.

It is not the kind of video that can stand alone, as information is not presented clearly enough – issues are identified and then only briefly described. It could contribute to a sex education programme by reinforcing information in a different visual medium (and one which many young people are familiar with and enjoy).

The video could be used in a variety of learning situations, viewed individually or in small groups; some topics will best be covered in single sex groups. It would benefit from viewing in short sections, topic by topic, with time for discussion and questions to ensure information has been absorbed and understood. The video has won national awards.

Your good health

FORMAT: Booklets (x10), illustrated
AUDIENCE: People with learning disabilities
PRICE: £30.00 + p&p (whole set); £5.00 + p&p (individual copies)
PRODUCER: Kidderminster: British Institute of Learning Disabilities (BILD), 1998
DISTRIBUTOR: BILD Publications, Plymbridge Distributors

This is a set of 10 booklets designed for people with learning disabilities to inform them about health issues and explain how to get help for a variety of health problems. They can be read by people with learning disabilities on their own or with help.

The booklets were developed by BILD and tested in conjunction with service users from self-advocacy groups in Worcester. They are easy to follow, combining clear illustrations with large print and straightforward language. This makes them accessible to some people with sight difficulties. The booklets promote a positive message about staying healthy, and place the power and responsibility for understanding and looking after themselves with people with learning disabilities.

Together the 10 booklets help to build up a coherent body of knowledge and reinforce simple messages about recognising symptoms. Each book provides a good deal of information about individual topics with instructions and checklists. The topics naturally fall into two groups.

The first group covers: if you are ill; using medicine safely; seeing and hearing; breathe easily; and looking after your teeth. These concentrate on basic health care, such as how to look after yourself and recognise when something is wrong, as well as what needs treatment and where to go for help, plus the dos and don'ts.

The second group focuses on health education and the topics include: eating and drinking; exercise; alcohol and smoking; coping with stress; and sex. These are packed with useful and sensible non-judgemental information to reassure and inform.

These booklets are essential for people with learning disabilities living both independently and in residential or private homes. They are also valuable for self-help and self-advocacy groups and could form the basis of training courses on healthy living. The advent of primary care groups has created a need for information to prepare consumers to take a more active part in healthcare planning. These booklets could be used as a foundation for participation by people with learning disabilities.

Your rights about sex

FORMAT: Booklet, 20-pages
AUDIENCE: People with learning disabilities
AUTHOR: McCarthy, M. and Cambridge, P.
PRICE: £5.00 + p&p
PRODUCER: Kidderminster: British Institute of Learning Disabilities (BILD) Publications, 1996
DISTRIBUTOR: BILD Publications, Plymbridge Distributors,
ISBN: 1 873791 52 6

This booklet aims to inform people with learning disabilities about some of their sexual rights. It is intended to be read by people with learning disabilities together with staff support and used as part of a longer programme of sex education. It covers issues such as privacy, masturbating, same sex relationships, sex education, and abuse.

The layout uses text and black-and-white line drawings. Each drawing has one of two symbols in the corner: a smiling face with a tick for sexual acts that are good or OK (for example, with a drawing of two people of the same sex hugging); or a cross and a frowning face for sexual acts that are a bad thing to do (for example, with a drawing of a man pulling a woman down on to a bed). Each page deals with a different issue. The language used is simple and the images are clearly drawn so as to convey feelings and events. This means that the booklet could be used with people without reading skills. None of the images show people having sex or show people's private parts, because, as the introduction says, 'These are private things and people get embarrassed. There are other books to explain about sex. You can see these and learn about these things if you have sex education.'

The booklet covers: masturbation; touching other people; choosing someone the same sex as you; sex education; privacy; having someone of the same sex to help you with washing and periods; saying no to sexual touching you do not want; and complaining when something is wrong. On the last page of the book, there is space for the name of someone the reader can ask to speak to privately about sex.

The focus of the booklet is on rights rather than sex education. It is not intended as a substitute for formal sex education or to replace informal discussions about sex.

It will probably encourage questions and discussion, and may highlight the need for further sex education. It could be used to help assess an individual's level of knowledge around sex and sexual rights, and might be a good springboard for further work on privacy. It could also fit into more general work on the rights of the individual.

Appendix 1
Reviewers and critical readers

The following reviewers and critical readers are thanked for their time and contribution to the original and ongoing development of this database.

Reviewers

The original search and review process was co-ordinated by Mental Health Media. The project team at Mental Health Media were:

Jerry Rothwell
Karen Mattison
Claudia Feldner
Heather Davis

The original reviewers also included:

Ruth Bailey
Heather Davis
Joanna Greenwell
Carolyn Hassan
Marion Janner
Mary Ryan
Andrew Shaer
Karen Shook
Jan Wyatt

Reviews were subsequently written by:

Jerry Rothwell, Mental Health Media
Naomi Richardson, Psychotherapist and Training and Education Consultant – Learning Disabilities
Daphne Welch, Training and Development – Learning Disabilities

Critical readers

Critical readers at the development stage included:

Andrew Bright, People First London

The late Dr Ann Craft, Department of Learning Disabilities, Queen's Medical Centre, Nottingham

Caroline Downs, Department of Learning Disabilities, Queen's Medical Centre, Nottingham

Paul Frazer, Day Centre Worker, The Grange Day Centre, London

Michelle McCarthy, The Tizard Centre, University of Kent

Christine Sibley, Headteacher, Beatrice Tate School, London

Hasu Morar, Senior Information Officer, Mencap

David Thompson, Sex Education Project for People with Learning Difficulties, Harperbury Hospital, Hertfordshire

Appendix 2
Distributors

Avanti Books

8 Parsons Green
Boulton Road
Stevenage
SG1 4QG
Tel: 01438 745876/350155
Fax: 01438 741131
e-mail: avantihil@aol.com

Boulton Hawker Films Ltd

Hadleigh
Ipswich IP7 5BG
Tel: 01473 822235
Fax: 01473 824519

British Educational Communications and Technology Agency (BECTA)

Special Educational Needs and Inclusion
Milburn Hill Road
Science Park
Coventry CV4 7JJ
Tel: 01203 416994
Fax: 01203 411418
e-mail: becta@becta.org.uk
Website: www.becta.org.uk

British Epilepsy Association

Anstey House
40 Hanover Square
Leeds LS3 1BE
Tel: 0113 243 9393

British Institute of Learning Disabilities (BILD) Publications

Plymbridge Distributors
Plymbridge House
Estover Road
Plymouth PL6 7PZ
Tel: 01752 202300
Fax: 01752 202333

Brook Advisory Centres

Education and Publications
165 Gray's Inn Road
London WC1X 8UD
Tel: 0171 833 8488
Fax: 0171 833 8182
e-mail: brookcentres@compuserve.com.uk

Centre for Studies on Inclusive Education

1 Redland Close
Elm Lane
Redland
Bristol BS6 6UE
Tel: 0117 923 8450;
Fax: 0117 923 8460
Tel: 0181 563 1664 (London)

Contact a Family

170 Tottenham Court Road
London W1P 0HA
Tel: 0171 383 3555

Down's Syndrome Association

155 Mitcham Road
London SW17 9PG
Tel: 0181 682 4001
Fax: 0181 682 4012

Durham County Priority Services NHS Trust

FAO Carol A. Charters
Community Team for Learning Disabilities
Upperthorpe
90 Woodland Road
Darlington DL3 7PZ
Tel: 01325 355440
Fax: 01325 382662

EMFEC

Robins Wood House
Robins Wood Road
Aspley
Nottingham NG8 3NH
Tel: 0115 929 3291
Fax: 0115 929 9392

Enable

6th Floor
7 Buchanan Street
Glasgow G1 3HL
Tel: 0141 226 4541
Fax: 0141 204 4398

Everyday Skills Packs

Dundee Healthcare NHS Trust
1 Edwards Street
Dundee DD1 5NS
Tel: 01382 346045
Fax: 01382 346040

Family Advice and Information Resource

25–27 West Nicholson Street
Edinburgh EH8 9DB
Tel: 0131 662 1962

Headon Productions

The Paul Building
Denison Road
Victoria Park
Manchester M14 5RX
Tel/Fax: 0161 225 7080

Healthwise Resource Department

1st Floor
Cavern Court
8 Matthew Street
Liverpool L2 6RE
Tel: 0151 227 4415
Fax: 0151 227 4019
e-mail: 100565.565@compuserve.com

Heinemann Educational

Customer Services
FREEPOST
P O Box 381
Oxford OX2 8BR
Tel: 01865 314320
Fax: 01865 314091
e-mail: bhuk.orders@repp.co.uk
Website: http://www.heinemann.co.uk

Home Farm Trust Trading

Merchant's House
Wapping Road
Bristol BS1 4RW
Tel: 0117 927 9746

Image in Action

8 Severn Terrace
Watchet
Somerset TA23 0AS
Tel/Fax: 01984 634242

James Stanfield and Co. Inc.

P O Box 41058
Santa Barbara
California 93140
USA
Tel: 001 805 897 1185
Fax: 001 805 897 1187

Jessica Kingsley Publishers Ltd

116 Pentonville Road
London N1 9JB
Tel: 0171 833 2307
Fax: 0171 837 2917

Learning Development Aids

Duke Street
Wisbech
Cambs PE13 2AE
Tel: 01945 463441
Fax: 01945 587361

Life Support Productions

PO Box 2127
London NW1 6RZ
Tel/Fax: 0171 723 7520

Magpie Productions

Dykes End
Ivychurch
Romney Marsh
Kent TN29 0AU
Tel: 01797 344623

Manchester People First

c/o VAM
Fourways House
57 Hilton Street
Manchester M1 2EJ
Tel: 0161 236 6418
Fax: 0161 228 0464

Mental Health Media

The Resource Centre
356 Holloway Road
London N7 6PA
Tel: 0171 700 0100
Fax: 0171 700 0099

The National Autistic Society

393 City Road
London EC1V 1NE
Tel: 0171 833 2299
Fax: 0171 833 9666
e-mail: nas@clvsl.ulcc.ac.uk
Website: www.oneworld.org/autism-uk/

The Norah Fry Research Centre

University of Bristol
3 Priory Road
Bristol BS8 1TX
Tel: 0117 928 9814
Fax: 0117 946 6553

The Open University

Learning Materials Sales Office (LMSO)
The Open University
PO Box 188
Milton Keynes MK7 6DH
Tel: 01908 653140/653338 (answerphone)
Fax: 01908 654320

Pavilion Publishing Ltd

Customer Services
8 St George's Place
Brighton
East Sussex BN1 4GB
Tel: 01273 623222
Fax: 01273 625526
Website: http://www.pavpub.com/publications/plearn.htm\sic

People First

Instrument House
207-215 Kings Cross Road
London WC1X 9DB
Tel: 0171 713 6400
Fax: 0171 833 1880

Resources for Learning

Woodward Court
19 Park Drive
Heaton
Bradford BD9 4DS
Tel: 01274 544155
Fax: 01274 549391

Rhondda Community Support Team

Llwynypia Day Centre
Llwynypia Road
Tonypandy
Mid Glamorgan CF40 2JQ
Tel: 01443 439266
Fax: 01443 440005

Richard Ives

23 Heathville Road
London N19 3AL
Tel: 0171 263 0510
Fax: 0171 561 1595
e-mail: richard-ives@compuserve.com

RightTrack

Tetford House
Teford
Lincolnshire LN9 6QQ
Tel/Fax: 01507 533639

Royal College of Psychiatrists

Book Sales
17 Belgrave Square
London SW1X 8PG
Tel: 0171 235 2351 ext. 146
Fax: 0171 245 1231
e-mail: booksales@rcpsych.ac.uk
Website: http://www.rcpsych.ac.uk

Skills for People

Speak for Ourselves (START!)
Key House
Tankerville Place
Newcastle upon Tyne NE2 3AT
Tel: 0191 281 8737

Speakup Self Advocacy

43 Holm Flatt Street
Parkgate
Rotherham S62 6HJ
Tel: 01709 710199

Swindon People First

The Health Hydro
Milton Road
Swindon SN1 5JA
Tel: 01793 465630
Fax: 01793 465666

Taskmaster Ltd

Morris Road
Leicester LE2 6BR
Tel: 0116 270 4286

Them Wifies

109 Pilgrim Street
Newcastle upon Tyne NE1 6QF
Tel: 0191 261 4090

Two Ten Productions

Building 150
Thorpe Arch Trading Estate
Wetherby LS23 7EH

Valley and Vale Community Arts Ltd

Blaengarw Workmen's Hall
Blaengarw (near Bridgend)
Mid Glamorgan CF32 8AW
Tel: 01656 871911
Fax: 01656 870507

Viewpoint Project

FAO Carol Armistead
Dorset Healthcare NHS Trust
Learning Disabilities Service
Kings Park Community Hospital
Gloucester Road
Boscombe
Bournemouth BH7 6JE
Tel: 01202 303757

Winslow Press

Telford Road
Bicester
Oxfordshire OX6 0TS
Tel: 01869 244644
Fax: 01869 320040
e-mail: info@winslow-press.co.uk
Website: www.winslow-press.co.uk

You and Me Yoga Centre

The Cottage
Burton-in-Kendal
Carnforth
Lancs LA6 1ND
Tel: 01524 782103

Youth Work Press

17–23 Albion Street
Leicester LE1 6GD
Tel: 0116 285 6789
Fax: 0116 247 1043